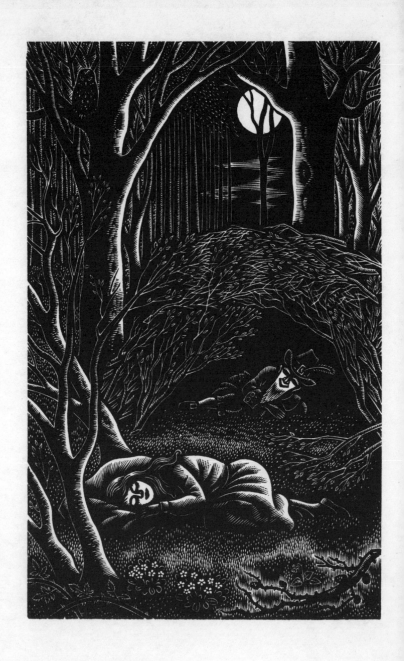

GRIMMS' OTHER TALES

A NEW SELECTION BY WILHELM
HANSEN: TRANSLATED & EDITED
BY RUTH MICHAELIS-JENA AND
ARTHUR RATCLIFF: ILLUSTRATED
WITH TEN WOOD-ENGRAVINGS
BY GWENDA MORGAN

SOUTH BRUNSWICK
NEW YORK: A. S. BARNES AND CO.
LONDON: THOMAS YOSELOFF LTD

© Thomas Yoseloff Ltd, 1959

This edition of *Grimms' Other Tales* follows the original Golden Cockerel Press edition, designed and produced by Christopher Sandford. Composition is in Poliphilus type. The illustrations are copied from the wood engravings in that edition. Presswork and binding are by the Kingsport Press. The jacket was designed by Lauretta Sellitti, and the book was published in this edition in August, 1966.

A. S. Barnes and Co., Inc.
South Brunswick, New Jersey

Thomas Yoseloff Ltd
18 Charing Cross Road
London, W C 2, England

Library of Congress Catalogue Card Number: AC66-10764

6482
Printed in the United States of America

CONTENTS

6

INTRODUCTION

THERE is one pleasure in standing before the completed masterpiece of a painter, and another in seeing his early sketches for the same picture. In the latter experience it is the unstudied immediacy that captivates us and affords, in some degree, the feeling of having shared in the genesis of the work. The same is true of writers.

When, some years ago, on a visit to Western Germany, we were allowed by Herr Wilhelm Hansen to see a batch of stories from the extensive resources of the Grimm collection, which we then followed up by a visit to Tübingen University to inspect the *Nachlass* of the Brothers Grimm, we felt that we were gaining an intimacy with *The Household Tales*, hitherto missed. Eventually Herr Hansen put his material at our disposal; and out of this has developed the present selection of little-known fairy-tales collected by the Brothers Grimm.

These tales are little known in the sense that some were published by the Grimms in their first edition of *The Household Tales* (1812) but later omitted and not translated by Taylor (1823); others were printed only in the Grimms' very full notes, available to scholars in the standard edition of Bolte-Polivka, *Anmerkungen zu den Kinder- und Hausmärchen der Brüder Grimm*; yet others come from the original manuscript given by the Grimms to Clemens Bretano and afterwards known as the Oelenberg MS (edited by Joseph Lefftz, and now out of print); and the remainder are still in manuscript among the Grimm Papers at present in the keeping of the University of Tübingen, though some have been printed at hazard in various German folklore periodicals. None is included in the definitive edition of *The Household Tales*; and one may well venture to think that all will be new to the common reader in the English-speaking world. Indeed Taylor himself, in the Preface to his translation of the tales wrote: 'The nature and immediate design of the present publication exclude the introduction of some of those stories which would, in a literary point of view, be most curious. With a view to variety, they [the translators] have wished rather to avoid than to select those, the leading incidents of which are already familiar to the English reader, and have therefore often deprived themselves of the interest which comparison would afford. There were also many stories of great merit, and tending highly to the elucidation of ancient mythology, customs, and opinions, which the scrupulous fastidiousness of modern taste, especially in works likely to attract the attention of youth, warned them to pass by. If they should ever be encouraged to resume their task, they might undertake it with different, and more serious objects.'

It may be said that the translators of the present volume have started where Taylor left off.

These tales moreover have gained immensely in interest in the light of latter-day developments in the study of folklore. Up to the early nineteenth century, when the Brothers Grimm were the main agents in changing the tradition, fairy-tales were looked upon as something childish and inferior, at best to be used as raw material for prettifying. But to the Grimms they were something more real and vital, part of a forgotten past, to be taken seriously, accurately recorded and collected scientific-ally. Traditional tales were basic folklore data, and the greater the number of variants assembled the greater would be the 'truth' of the final version. Variants occurred from district to district and from story-teller to story-teller: the untiring diligence of the two brothers procured and recorded them all. But not all were used; and others were at later stages discarded. The brothers were concerned above all with authenticity to the oral tradition as preserved on the lips of the common people: they resented intrusions of any sort that meant sophistication—yet it was diffi-cult always to distinguish these.

During their student days at the University of Marburg,

Savigny, the law professor, had kindled the brothers' interest in the legacy of the Middle Ages; and this interest flared up in the fire of Romanticism that swept across German letters. The Grimms were in close contact, indeed, with two of the Romantic leaders, Arnim and Brentano.

Quite young, and poor, the Grimms started their recording in neatly-written little notebooks, in which, first, they took down songs, legends and tales remembered from their own childhood, and next others obtained from relatives and friends. The notebooks might have remained permanently unprinted in the Grimms' desks had it not been for the active encouragement of Achim von Arnim. In a letter written twenty-five years later Wilhelm was to say: 'it was he [Arnim] who drove us to publication . . . of our collections he preferred the fairy-tales. He thought we should not hold on to them for too long before publication, because by our striving for completeness, the job might in the end be given up altogether.' Thus the enterprise was one of scholarship, not of the mere compilation of a story-book for children: they hit upon a world classic by accident.

It was at Christmas 1812 that the first volume of *The Household Tales* appeared, with a dedication to Bettina, Achim von Arnim's wife, on behalf of her little son. The critical reception was far from enthusiastic—many found the 'unimproved' stories wearisome—yet the book was an immediate success with the general public. Unmoved by either circumstance the two went on with their labour of love, Jacob, the scholar, closely concerned with problems of language, and Wilhelm, the creative writer, drawn to the rich imaginative potentialities of folklore. They had an instinctively right approach to a wide variety of people, both simple and high-born, to induce willing co-operation. They interviewed shepherds, peasants and tramps, visited old women in almshouses, and engaged in their enterprise members of the Hessian and Westphalian landed gentry met over the dinner-table. One of their more picturesque finds was an old soldier—a former sergeant of dragoons—who bartered his tales for gifts of discarded trousers.

Jacob's duties in the diplomatic service greatly widened their horizon and they began to exchange information with scholars all over Europe. A notable British connection was Sir Walter Scott, through whom they obtained some Scottish material. They also used literary sources, gleaning tales from early German manuscripts and the so-called Folk-Books. In fact, however, their greatest find was the Fairy-Tale-Wife of Niederzwehren near Cassel. They wrote of her as unequalled for retaining the old tales firmly in her mind in a pure and unspoilt form. She was a born storyteller. 'She recounts her stories,' wrote Wilhelm Grimm in the Preface to the 1815 volume, 'thoughtfully, accurately, with uncommon vividness and evident delight—first quite easily, but then, if required, over again, slowly.'

Many of their helpers took down stories for them, and their names are preserved in entries made in the Grimms' own copy of the first edition of the *Tales*: some are marked 'from Dortchen' (later Wilhelm's wife), and one 'Dortchen by the stove in the summer-house'—giving a flavour of true German *Gemütlichkeit*. The 'alte Marie' in the Wild's house, the von Haxthausens and the Hassenpflugs were ardent supporters.

Returning to the present collection of tales, we may speculate on the reasons for the Grimms not using them, or for rejecting them after the first edition, These appear twofold, and on the surface contradictory: for some were left out because Wilhelm judged their story interest insufficient to hold the attention, or the incidents too fragmentary, but others because they were only too exciting—sometimes horrifying—for young readers; while still others Jacob, the purist scholar, thought too '*interpoliert*', 'improved' and 'embellished' and therefore suspect.

Today the stark recordings of folklore, without veneer, interest us again, so that even the Grimms' strictly limited rewriting may seem too much and their rejected material sometimes preferable.

It is timely therefore that some of the unused, and relatively not 'written-up', tales collected by the Grimms should be made available in English. Many of these are delightful in themselves; the rest, though somewhat cruder in form than the well-known ones, exercise a powerful appeal through their sudden transitions and unsoftened violences. These stories give us entry into the very workshop of the Grimms: above all, they have a singularly wry or humorous or deeply touching or peasant-fancy interest of their own. More than ever, in this materialistic age, we need reminders of the enduring stuff of which human nature is made.

Edinburgh 1956   RUTH MICHAELIS-JENA
                                                   ARTHUR RATCLIFF

MAKE-ME-SHUDDER

THERE was once a lad—his father was a blacksmith—who was quite fearless, and even when he was taken to the grave-yard and other fearsome places he wasn't a bit afraid.

One day his father said to him, 'If you were to go out into the world, you'd soon learn what fear is.' So the lad went away, and at nightfall happened to come to a village; but as by that hour every house was shut, he lay down under the gallows. When he saw a man hanging there, he said to him, 'What have they hanged you for?' The man answered, 'I am innocent. The schoolmaster stole the little bell from the collection bag, and blamed me for it. If you will help me to an honest burial, I'll give you a stick and with it you can knock down any ghost. The schoolmaster has the bell hidden under a big slab in his cellar.'

On hearing this, the lad got up and went back to the village. He knocked at the schoolmaster's door, but though the man got up he wouldn't open as he was afraid. The lad called out, 'If you don't open your door, I'll break it down.' Then the man did open it, and the lad grabbed him in his night-shirt, flung him over his shoulder and bore him off to the judge's house. There he cried, 'Open the door—I've brought you a thief!' The judge came out, whereupon the lad said to him, 'Cut the poor wretch down that's hanging on the gallows—he's innocent. Hang this fellow in his place, for he's the one that stole the bell from the collection-bag—it's in his cellar under a big slab.'

The judge sent someone to look, and he found the little bell, so the schoolmaster had to admit the theft. The judge then gave the order: 'Cut the innocent man down from the gallows and give him honest burial. Then hang the thief in his place.'

The following night the young blacksmith went back to the gallows. The innocent man was already in a Christian grave, but his ghost appeared to the boy and handed over the promised stick.

'Now,' said the young blackmsith, 'I'll go out into the world and look for Make-me-Shudder.'

The lad chanced to arrive in a town where there was a haunted castle that none dared enter, and the King, hearing that some-one had come to the town who was afraid of nothing, sent for him and said, 'If you can break the spell binding the haunted castle, I'll make you so rich your wealth will know no end.' 'Gladly,' answered the lad, 'if somebody will show me how to get there.'

'I must tell you,' added the King, 'there are no keys to it.'

'Don't need any,' replied the lad; 'I'll get in all right.'

Then they took him to the castle; and when he reached the outer gate he knocked at it with his stick, it sprang open at once, and on the inside he found the keys to the whole castle. First he unlocked the inner door. The moment it opened a horde of ghosts came out, one with horns, another spitting fire, and all as black as pitch. The young blacksmith muttered to himself, 'Queer folk and no mistake!—they look like charcoal-burners. I'll take them home with me and they can tend my father's furnace.' Then of a sudden they all set on him; but he knocked them down, six at a blow, with his stick, seized hold of them, and flung them into a room from which they couldn't escape.

Picking the keys up again, he unlocked the second door. This time he found a coffin that had a body inside it, and close by a great black poodle was lying with a red-hot chain round its neck. The lad marched in, tapped on the coffin and called, 'What are you doing here, old charcoal-burner?' At these words the dead man rose and tried to frighten him, but he roared,

14

'Get out of here!' and as the corpse was slow to obey he grabbed hold of it and thrust it into the room along with the rest. Going back to the second room he picked up the red-hot chain, wound it round his body, then shouted to the black dog, 'Get out of here!' However, it didn't budge, but spat out fire. The lad then cried, 'If you can do that, I'm certainly taking you home with me—you too can help Father make up the furnace!' But in a flash the dog vanished—it may well have been the Devil himself!

One small key was left still, for the last door. On opening this he found twelve black ghosts, horned and fiery of breath. Again he knocked them down with his stick; then flung them out, dropped them into a water-tank, and put the lid on it. 'Well, that's that,' crowed the lad; 'but my! it's hot work, I must get something to drink.' He went down to the cellar, drew some old wine from the cask, and felt much better.

Meanwhile, away in his castle, the King was anxious about the lad. 'I wonder what can have happened to him,' he exclaimed, and sent his confessor to find out, for nobody else would have dared go to the haunted castle. Now the priest was hunchbacked and bent. He knocked at the castle gate and the young black-smith came out, but seeing the priest misshapen and in his long black coat he cried, 'Here's another one left! What do you want, you hunchbacked old devil?' Then he shut him up too.

Now the King waited one more day, but when the holy man still failed to return he sent a company of soldiers to take the castle by force. Seeing them the lad cried, 'Some live men, at last! I'd better open the gates.' Then the soldiers asked him why he had locked up the King's confessor, and he answered, 'My dear boys, why did he come here rigged out in a black coat!' But the soldiers next asked, 'What can we tell the King?' 'Tell His Majesty to come himself: the castle is all cleared!'

On hearing the glad news the King set out at once, and found in the castle heaps of precious stones, fine silverware and casks of rare old wine. This rich treasure was now his own again.

In thankfulness he ordered a suit of the purest gold for the young blacksmith; but the lad said, 'No, thank you, Your Majesty, I do not want it—it's only a fool's dress,' and pushed it aside. 'But,' he added, 'I won't leave the castle before Your Majesty has shown me Make-me-Shudder: you *must* know the fellow.'

Then, to reward the young blacksmith, the King had a white linen smock made, with lots of gold pieces sewn into it; but saying, 'It's too heavy for me,' the lad threw it off and put his old smock on again. Once more he thought, 'But before I go home to my Father I simply must see Make-me-Shudder;' and he picked up his stick and went before the King.

So the King took him and showed him a great cannon. The lad gazed at it, walked round it on every side, and asked, 'What on earth is this, Your Majesty?'

'Just stand back a little,' ordered the King; and he had the cannon loaded and fired.

When the lad heard the dreadful bang, he cried, 'Yes, to be sure, Your Majesty, that really *is* Make-me-Shudder! Now, at last, I've seen him.'

And he went home contented.

THE FROG PRINCE

THERE once lived a King who had three daughters. In the courtyard of his castle was a crystal-clear well, to which, one hot summer's day, the eldest Princess went down to fetch a glass of water. She filled the glass, but as she was holding it up against the sun she noticed to her surprise that the water was all muddy. She was about to pour it back again when she saw a frog in the well; and what was more he raised his head, sprang on to the stone ledge, and sang:

> 'If you will be my true love dear
> The water I will soon make clear;
> But if you won't my true love be,
> Naught but mud you'll ever see.'

'Pooh!' scoffed the Princess, 'who'd be the sweetheart of a nasty frog anyway?' And she ran off to tell her sisters about the queer well-frog who had turned the water muddy.

The second sister, made curious by this story, then ran down to fill her glass. Again the water was muddy, so that she did not care to drink it, and as before the frog sprang on to the ledge and sang:

> 'If you will be my true love dear
> The water I will soon make clear.'

'You're the very fellow I want!' laughed the Princess; and then ran off.

At last the third sister, in her turn, went down to drink. But she fared no better, and to her, too, the frog sang:

> 'If you will be my true love dear
> The water I will soon make clear.'

'Yes, yes,' replied the Princess, 'of course I'll be your sweetheart; only do make the water clear, please.' But she was thinking 'What does it matter, after all, to promise?—it pleases him, and a silly frog couldn't be my sweetheart anyway!' The frog had now jumped back into the well; and when the Princess stooped down the second time, the water was so clear that the sun seemed to sparkle through it for sheer joy. The Princess drank her fill of it, and took some to her sisters, exclaiming, 'Really, what fools you were to be afraid of a mere frog!' Then she thought no more about the matter, and went to bed that night in the best of spirits.

She had lain down just a little while, and was still not asleep, when suddenly she heard a shuffling noise at her door and a voice singing:

'Open the door, my Princess dear,
Open the door, for I am here.
Do you remember what you said
Down on the green at the well-head?—
That you would be my true love dear
Were I to make the water clear!'

'Ah-ha, that must be my frog lover!' cried the Princess. 'Well, as I gave my word, I suppose I'd better open the door.'

So up she got, left the door ajar, and lay down again. The frog sprang after her into the room and on to the bed, where he lay all night at her feet; but as morning broke he leapt down again and out of the door.

The next night, when the Princess lay in bed, she heard the shuffling again and the little song at the door. She duly opened, and as before the frog stayed at her feet until daybreak.

The third night, the same thing happened. But this time the Princess exclaimed, 'Now, look here, this is the very last time I'm going to let you in, so please, no more of it.' Then the frog sprang under the pillow, and the Princess fell asleep.

But when she woke next morning, ready for the frog to leap down, she beheld a handsome young Prince standing before her, and saying, 'Dearest Princess, I was wickedly enchanted and changed into a frog, but by your promise to be my true love you have broken the spell.'

So they went together to the King, who, after hearing their story, gave them his blessing and the wedding soon took place. But the two sisters were cross with themselves for not having taken the frog as their sweetheart.

THE NIGHTINGALE AND THE
SLOW-WORM

ONCE upon a time there were a nightingale and a slow-worm, who had only one eye apiece; and they lived contentedly together in the same house for a long while.

Now one day the nightingale was invited to a wedding, and he said to the slow-worm, 'I've been asked to a wedding, but I don't like going with one eye. Will you be good enough to lend me yours? I'll give it you back tomorrow.'

Out of sheer kindness the slow-worm agreed.

But the next day, when the nightingale was home again, he was so pleased to have two eyes in his head, and be able to see on both sides, that he wouldn't return the borrowed eye to the poor slow-worm. Then the slow-worm swore to revenge himself on the nightingale, his children and his children's children.

The nightingale only sneered, saying, 'Get along and whistle for it!

> 'I'll build my nest in the linden tree
> So high, so high, so high,
> That from now unto eternity
> You'll never find your eye!'

So from that day to this, nightingales have had two eyes and slow-worms have been blind; but wherever a nightingale nests, a slow-worm lurks in the bushes below, awaiting his chance to bore holes in the eggs of the enemy and suck them dry.

BEAUTIFUL CATHARINELLA

LONG long ago, in a village in Italy, lived a man and his wife who had a daughter called Catharinella. She had such lovely fair hair that words cannot describe how beautiful were the plaits wound round her head.

The father was a soldier, and just when a new baby was to be born he was called away to the wars. At that time the mother was always hungry for parsley, and soon had eaten up all there was in her garden. Next she went the round of her neighbours' gardens, till at length there wasn't the tiniest sprig of parsley left in the whole village. The only bit remaining near grew in the garden of an ogre who lived in a great palace outside the village.

The poor woman wept and was very unhappy because she feared that she and her unborn child would die of starvation. Seeing the sad state her dear mother was in, Catharinella too was sad, and at last decided to go every day and steal as much parsley from the ogre's garden as her mother wanted. When the ogre went round each night to see how his garden grew, he found the parsley plants getting fewer and fewer; and he shook his head angrily, while his long beard swept the box-hedge lining the beds on both sides. As this did not seem to mend matters much, he at last strewed ashes secretly along the path.

So in the morning, when Catharinella went as usual to fetch her mother's parsley, the ashes stuck to her little slippers, and the ogre easily traced the way to her cottage. He followed her in, and appearing to be very angry he threatened that unless she came to the palace as his servant he would eat her. The poor mother sobbed bitterly, not wanting the girl to go; but when the ogre promised that no harm would come to her—he would even let her pick each day all the parsley her mother wanted— it was agreed, and Catharinella departed with her new master.

Now the ogre was not really as fierce and wicked as he looked, but just a little lazy; and when he came home in the evening after eating heartily he hated to climb the stairs. So he shouted from below the window, 'Catharinella, Catharinella, let your golden plaits down and lift me into the house,' and the girl did so; and that was all the work she had to do. She enjoyed an easy life, with plenty to eat and drink; and she had lots of fun talking to the furniture, for it was enchanted.

As he got older, the ogre grew lazier and lazier, till he didn't want to do a thing for himself, and even took in a young man to help with the magic. This was a smart, nice-looking fellow, who had not got a long beard, nor did he wait long at the door when *he* wished to see Catharinella—no, he leapt up the stairs drawn by the beautiful golden plaits in quite a different way from the ogre! Every day the ogre seemed heavier and heavier to the girl, and she disliked him so much that she was well pleased when the young wizard offered to conjure up a coach and horses to take them away.

Soon everything was ready for their flight, but as all the pieces of furniture could talk the pair were afraid they might blab and the old ogre would learn where they had gone—and before they were far enough off for him not to catch up with them. So they thought and they thought what they could do to keep the furniture quiet. In the end Catharinella decided she would cook a great potful of macaroni and treat them, lock, stock and barrel, to this tasty dish. She soon set to work, and when the macaroni was cooked she stood the great pot in the main hall and invited everything in the house to eat its fill. It must have been a funny sight indeed to see chairs, settles, tables and all, come running! —mirrors and pictures flying down off the walls; stout old cupboards stumbling along; china sets and glasses tripping lightly —all to enjoy the treat. They made a dreadful din, all the big and little mouths busily munching, and even the great pot itself now and again gulping down some of its own contents. When they had eaten all they could, they promised to say nothing that would betray the kind folk who had fed them. And in fact all would have been well, if an old besom in a corner of the attic had not been forgotten. He went stumping round the house in a rage, shouting all the time, 'They've all eaten macaroni—but they've forgotten me!' In vain Catharinella tried to soothe him down, but there was nothing she could do save get away as quickly as possible with her young man. This she did, not taking a thing with her but a brush, a comb and a mirror, to keep her hair tidy.

That night, when the ogre came home, he shouted as usual, 'Catharinella, Catharinella, let your golden plaits down and lift me into the house.' But there was no answer. When at last he grew impatient and forced the door, the old besom came to meet him, all tousle-haired and excited, struggling to pour out everything; but as he had said nothing else all day, he could only repeat, 'They've all eaten macaroni—but they've forgotten me!' The ogre grasped that something was wrong, and went round asking the other household things to tell, but all were so stuffed with food that they gave nothing away. Yet he soon got an idea of what had happened.

He tucked up his cloak, tied three knots in his long beard—so that it couldn't get in his way in running—and took up the chase. In a short time he sighted the pair in the distance, in the magic coach. Nearer and nearer he drew, till he could reach out for Catharinella, who was just looking out of the coach window. In her panic she flung her comb at him—and in a trice it changed into iron bars, which caught the ogre's beard as he tried to get across. In the end he succeeded and almost clutched the coach; but now Catharinella flung out her brush, which instantly turned into a thorn-bush. The ogre's beard got caught again, and his cloak torn; but once more he managed to struggle through and come near the coach. Then Catharinella threw out the mirror.

It turned into a lake, and drowned the ogre.

HANS FRANK

THERE was once a woman who had two daughters, one
her own and the other a step-daughter, and they lived
together in a house that was haunted, indeed so much so that
they had to go away—the ghosts never left them in peace, day
or night.

Now the mother had no love for her step-daughter and dearly
wished to get rid of her, so one night she bade her visit the old
house, thinking the ghosts would soon finish her off. Not to
arouse the girl's suspicion, she gave her bacon, flour and milk,
that she mightn't starve; and the moment the girl got to the old
house she went straight to the kitchen, lit the fire and began
baking pancakes. She wasn't afraid at all.

While she was busy someone knocked at the kitchen door,
and the girl called, 'Who's there?'

A voice came back:

> 'I'm Hans Frank so grand,
> With seven gates to my land
> And my hat so tall:
> Open the door, once and for all.'

At this the girl opened the door and in walked a tall fellow,
closing the door behind him. The girl went on with her baking,
and tall Hans Frank watched her in silence. When she was
done he walked in front of her to the next room, stood by the
table and said:

> 'I'm Hans Frank so grand,
> With seven gates to my land
> And my hat so tall:
> Lay the table, once and for all.'

Then the girl put the pancakes on the table, and Hans Frank
sat down and cleared the lot. Meantime the girl went off to bed;

but when he had finished his meal he stood beside her, saying:

> 'I'm Hans Frank so grand,
> With seven gates to my land
> And my hat so tall:
> Open the bed, once and for all.'

Then he lay down and they both fell asleep.

Next morning, when the girl got up and went into the other room, she found bag after bag chockful of money; and Hans Frank said, 'That's all yours for looking after me so well.'

The step-mother, of course, was dying to know what had happened, so at daybreak she was outside the door to see if the ghosts had finished her step-daughter off. She peeped in at the window and said, 'Hey, are you dead or alive?' The girl replied cheerfully, 'Just look, Mother, this money—it's all mine.' Taken aback by the news, the step-mother put on a friendly face and helped the girl carry the bags home.

Her own daughter, when she saw how things had turned out, thought to herself, 'Well, if it's as easy as all that, I'll try staying in the haunted house myself.' The same night she went; and likewise set to baking pancakes in the kitchen. While she was still busy Hans Frank arrived and asked her to open the door. The girl replied, 'I'm not at everybody's beck and call!—folks who want to come in here can open the door for them-selves.'

So Hans Frank had to open the door for himself; and he stood for a while watching the girl. When he walked into the other room, she followed him and sat down to eat, and after Hans Frank had said his say as with the first girl, she replied, 'I've got nothing for other folk. If you want something to eat, you can get it for yourself.' And she flounced off to bed.

Then when Hans Frank said his say beside her bed, the girl answered, 'Nobody can come into my bed—but you can lie underneath.' And she went off to sleep.

Now next morning when the mother came along and called, 'Hey, my child, have you too got lots of money?' Hans Frank replied, 'Heavens, what a girl! See—there hangs your little daughter! And don't dare come back here!'

Now when the mother saw her daughter's body hanging where Hans Frank had strung her up in the night for her mean‚ ness, she ran off home directly, and wild with rage drove her step‚daughter out of the house. But the money she kept, and the poor girl took nothing with her but a pillow to sleep on at night.

Then the girl went into the woods and made herself a little hut of branches. When it was finished, there came a manikin who asked her to give him shelter. 'The hut is only big enough for one,' the girl said, 'but you can have it, and I'll lie outside, if only you will see that no harm comes to me.' The manikin promised, and they lay down to rest, the manikin in the hut and the girl outside.

In the morning when the girl woke up, she found herself in a splendid bed hung with many curtains, lovely to look at. There she was, in a fine big hall quite wonderful to behold; and on the other side, in a bed as splendid as her own, was a charm‚ ing Prince. The girl got up at once ready to flee, but servants appeared and bade her stay; only then did she notice that the hall was part of a great castle.

The manikin was really an enchanted Prince, whose castle had once stood on the very spot where the girl had built her hut, but she had now lifted the spell from both Prince and castle. Not long after he married her, and they held a great wedding feast, which lasted for three days.

I was there myself. My gown was of butter and my bonnet of paper. My slippers were of glass. As I came home from the wedding, the sun peeped round the corner and my gown of butter melted. My paper bonnet caught on a nail, and when I knocked against a stone my glass slippers broke into a thousand splinters. So I became my old self again.

And now I'll climb the stairs—and let him tell the next tale who dares.

THE PRINCESS ON THE GLASS MOUNTAIN

THERE was once a Princess under a spell no one could break as she was banished to the top of a glass mountain. One day a young lad came into the inn hard by, and a boiled chicken was placed before him. So he took all the chicken bones and walked to the foot of the glass mountain, where he pushed one little bone in after another, and so climbed upwards.

When he had only one more step to go, he fell short of a tiny chicken-bone. So he cut off his little finger, stuck that into the glass mountain, stepped on it—and set the Princess free.

DEATH AND THE GOOSE-HERD

ONCE upon a time a poor herd was trudging along the bank of a wide and rapid river as he watched over a flock of white geese, when Death came across the water. The goose-herd asked Death whence he had come and whither he was going.

'I have come from the water,' answered Death, 'and I am going out of this world.'

'But how can one go out of this world?' asked the poor herd.

Death explained that one had to cross the river to the other world.

'I'm sick and tired of this life,' said the goose-herd; 'so will you take me across, Master Death?'

But Death said, 'Your time has not yet come, and besides I have other things to do.'

Not far off lived a miser who lay on his bed at night scheming how to gain still more riches. Death took *him* to the great water, and pushed him in, and as the miser couldn't swim he was drowned before he reached the other side. His cats and dogs, running after him, were drowned too.

Some days later Death returned to the goose-herd, and found him merrily singing.

'Will you come with me now?' he asked.

The herd was quite willing, and soon got to the other side, his white geese with him, now changed into white sheep.

The goose-herd looked at the goodly land around him. He learnt that shepherds there were made Kings; and while he was still looking he saw the ancient shepherds Abraham, Isaac and Jacob coming towards him. They set a royal crown upon his head, and took him to the shepherds' castle—and there the poor goose-herd dwells to this very day.

THE PHOENIX

ONE DAY a rich man walking by a riverside saw a little box come floating on the water. He fished it out, and when he took the lid off he found a baby inside. So he carried the child home to have him brought up in his own house.

Now the factor, who looked after his lands, took a dislike to the child. One day he put him in a boat on the river, and when they were right in the middle he himself jumped out and swam to the shore, but the child was left behind, alone in the boat, which floated down the river till it came to a mill. There the miller saw the child, and taking pity lifted him and took him to be brought up at his house.

Later, the factor happened to come to the mill, and seeing at

27

once who the boy was, took him away. Then he asked the lad to carry a letter to his wife, and it said: 'Kill the bearer of this letter instantly.' On his way through the wood the lad chanced to meet with an old man who said, 'Just let me see that letter you have there, will you.' Then the old man took it in his hand, merely turned it over and gave it back, but the letter now read: 'Marry our daughter to the bearer of this letter instantly.' And so it fell out.

When the factor heard the news he was wild with rage, and said, 'Not so fast! Before you get my daughter you must fetch me three feathers from the Phoenix.' So the youth set out to find the bird.

It chanced that at the same spot in the wood he again met with the old man, who said, 'Walk on the whole day, and in the evening you will come to a tree. You will see two doves perched on it, and they will tell you what to do next.'

In the evening the youth came to the tree, and there sat the two doves. The first dove said, 'He who seeks the Phoenix bird must walk on for a whole day, and in the evening he will come to a locked gate.' Then the second, 'Under this tree he will find a golden key, and with it he can open the gate.'

The boy found the key and opened the gate. Behind it sat two men, and the one said, 'He who seeks the Phoenix bird must walk far over the high mountain, and at length he will come to a castle.'

On the evening of the third day the youth at length got to the castle. There he found a little white lady, who said, 'What do you want here?' 'I should like three feathers from the Phoenix bird,' he replied.

'Then you are in danger of your life,' she said, 'for if the Phoenix catches sight of you he will eat you up, hair and all. However, I'll see if I can get you the three feathers. The Phoenix comes here every day, and I have to comb him with a fine comb. Quick!—get under the table!' Luckily the table was covered

with a cloth, which hung all round; for just then the Phoenix
bird came in, sat on the table and said, 'I spy, I spy the flesh of
man!'

'Nonsense!' answered the little lady, 'you can see for yourself
there's nobody here.'

'Well, then, you can comb me now,' said the Phoenix. While
the little white lady was combing him, he dozed off, and as soon
as he was sound asleep, she took hold of a feather, plucked it,
and dropped it under the table. At this the Phoenix awoke,
saying, 'Why do you comb so hard? I dreamt a man was here,
who plucked one of my feathers.' But the white lady soothed
him down. Thus it happened a second time and a third; and
the youth got his three feathers.

So in the end he went back home and married his bride.

PUSS-IN-BOOTS

THERE was once a miller who had three sons, his mill, a
donkey—and a cat. The sons worked the mill, the donkey
fetched the corn and took back the flour, while the cat caught
the mice.

When he died, the miller left all he had to his three sons: the
eldest got the mill, the second the donkey, and the third just the
cat, as there was nothing else left. The boy felt very sad and said
to himself, 'Well, that's downright unlucky! My elder brother
can work the mill, the other one can ride the donkey, but what
can I do—with a cat? If I get a pair of fur gloves out of his coat,
that'll be about all!'

'Now listen to me,' broke in the cat, who had understood
everything; 'you needn't go and kill me for a paltry pair of
gloves out of my fur! No; instead, get a pair of boots made for
me, so that I can go about amongst people, and soon enough
you'll get your reward.'

To hear the cat run on like this came as a shock to the young miller, but, as the cobbler was passing just at that moment, he called him in and told him to measure the cat for a pair of boots. When they were ready, the cat put them on; then he picked up a sack, filled the bottom with corn, and tied a string round the neck so as to pull it to. Then, flinging the sack over his shoulder, he strutted out of the house on two legs, just like a man.

Now the King who ruled the country at that time had a great liking for partridges, but there were few to be got. Plenty lived in the woods all right, but they were such shy birds that one couldn't get near enough for a shot. All this the cat knew, and he had a mind to see what he could do. So, when he reached the woods, he opened the sack, scattered some of the corn, and stretched the string along the grass to end up behind the hedge, where he lay hid. Soon the partridges came running up, they found the corn, and one after another hopped into the sack. Once a goodly number were safely inside, the cat pulled the string. Then he came out of hiding and killed all the trapped birds.

Next, swinging the sack over his shoulder, he went straight to the royal castle.

'Halt!' cried the guards. 'Where are you going?'

'To see the King,' answered the cat gruffly.

'Are you mad—a cat going to see the King!'

'Let him go,' said one; 'the King is often bored, and the cat may chance to amuse him with his purring.'

When the cat stood before the King, he made a low curtsey and said, 'My master, Count ——' (here he gave a long and noble name) 'presents his humble respects to Your Majesty, and hopes you will be pleased to accept a few partridges he has just caught in his snares.'

Surprised to see such fine fat partridges, the King scarcely knew what to say for joy. He ordered the cat to be given as much gold from the royal chest as he could carry in his sack, adding,

'Take that to your master, and thank him right heartily for his gift.'

Meantime the poor miller's son sat at his window, his head resting on his hand, thinking how he had now spent all he possessed on the cat's boots, and wondering what the cat could possibly bring him in return. Just then the cat came in, flung down the sack, untied the string, and shook the gold out on the floor in front of the youth.

'There, that is for the boots,' said the cat, 'and the King sends his greeting and hearty thanks.'

The miller lad was delighted to behold such riches, but could not see how this wonder had come about. But the cat, while taking his boots off, told him the whole story, adding, 'Now you've got plenty of money, but what you see isn't all; for to-morrow I'll put my boots on again and you'll be richer still. Besides, I've told the King that you are a Count!'

The next day the cat set out hunting once more in his fine boots, as he had promised, and brought another full bag to the King. And so it went on, day after day, the cat each time bringing home a sackful of gold. The King indeed grew so to like him that the cat could go in and out quite freely, and roam about the castle to his heart's content.

One day the cat was standing in the Royal Kitchen, warming himself beside the hearth, when the coachman rushed in and shouted in a fury, 'Hang the King and the Princess! I was just going down to the inn for a drink and a game of cards when I was ordered to drive the pair of them round the lake.'

Hearing this the cat slunk home and said to his master, 'If you want to become a real Count and a rich man, come with me down to the lake and have a bathe.'

The miller's son did not know what to make of this, all the same he got up and went after the cat. He then undressed and dived into the water, while the cat bundled up his clothes and hid them. Scarcely had he done this when the King came

32

driving along. Then the cat started a piteous moaning.

'O most noble King,' cried he, 'my master was bathing in the lake, but a thief came by and stole his clothes where they lay on the shore. My master, the noble Count, is in the water still, and daren't come out, yet if he stays in much longer he'll catch his death of cold.'

Hearing this, the King told his coachman to halt, and sent one of his men to rush back and fetch some of his royal garments. The 'Count' put on the stately clothes, and the King, believing him to be the sender of the partridges, felt kindly disposed and invited him to sit in the carriage next himself. Nor was the Princess put out at this, for the 'Count' was young and good-looking and pleased her very much.

Meantime the cat had gone on ahead to a large meadow where over a hundred farm-hands were busy hay-making.

'Tell me, good folk,' said he; 'who owns this meadow?'

'The Great Wizard,' they replied.

'Take heed, then,' he commanded, 'for soon the King will drive past. If he asks who owns this meadow, say, "The Count." If you don't every man Jack of you will be put to death.'

The cat went on again till he reached a cornfield so broad that one couldn't see over to the other side, and more than two hundred workers were busy cutting the corn.

'Tell me, good folk,' said he; 'who owns all this corn?'

'The Wizard,' came the reply.

'Take heed, then,' he commanded, 'for soon the King will drive past. If he asks who owns the corn, say "The Count." If you don't every man Jack of you will be put to death.'

At length the cat came to a fine wood where over three hundred workers were busy felling mighty oaks and sawing up the timber.

'Tell me, good folk; who owns all this wood?' said the cat.

'The Wizard,' came the reply.

'Take heed, then,' he commanded, 'for soon the King will

33

drive past. If he asks who owns the wood, say "The Count." If you don't every man Jack of you will be put to death.'

The cat walked on, and the people gazed after him. He looked so strange striding along in his boots, just like a man, that they were afraid of him. Soon he arrived at the castle of the Wizard, boldly walked in, and stood before him. The Wizard looked down on him with scorn and asked what he wanted, at which the cat curtsied and replied; 'I've heard tell that you can take the shape of any animal you like. As far as a dog, a fox or a wolf goes, I readily believe it, but to turn yourself into an elephant—well, I can't credit that! So I've come to see for myself.'

Puffed up to hear these words, the Wizard answered, 'Oh, that's child's play,' and the same moment he changed into an elephant.

'Well, that's something indeed; but what about a lion?'

'That's child's play, too,' answered the Wizard, and the same moment he stood before the cat in the shape of a lion.

Pretending to be terrified, the cat cried, 'It's beyond all belief —I shouldn't have thought it possible. But it would cap the trick if you could turn yourself into some small animal—say a mouse. You can outdo any other wizard alive, but this would be too much even for you.'

Such flattery won the wizard's heart, and he said, 'O yes, dear little pussycat, I can do that too.' Then at once he started running round the room in the shape of a mouse; but in a trice the cat sprang on him and gobbled him up.

Meanwhile the King had driven on with the Princess and the 'Count' till he reached the broad meadow.

'Tell me, good folk,' said the King; 'who owns the hay?'

'The Count, Your Majesty,' shouted everyone, just as the cat had ordered.

'Well, Count, you've certainly got some good land there,' said the King.

34

Then they came to the big cornfield.

'Tell me, good folk; who owns the corn?'

'The Count, Your Majesty,' came the reply.

'Well, Count, you certainly have a fine big estate there.'

Then they came to the wood.

'Tell me, good folk; who owns the timber?'

'The Count, Your Majesty,' came the reply.

More and more impressed the King said, 'You must be a rich man, Count. I don't think I've ever seen such a fine wood.'

At length they came to the castle. The cat stood at the top of the staircase, and when the carriage stopped below he jumped down and opened the door, saying, 'Your Majesty, you are now in the castle of my master the Count, who will be honoured all his life by your visit.'

The King stepped down from the carriage and marvelled at the great castle, which seemed even bigger and nobler than his own. The 'Count' then led the Princess up the staircase and into the hall flashing with gold and precious stones.

Soon afterwards the Princess was betrothed to the 'Count'; and later, when the King died, the 'Count' came to the throne, and Puss-in-Boots was made his Minister of State.

SIMPLE HANS

THERE was once a King who lived happily with his only daughter. Then one day, to everyone's surprise, the Princess bore a child, though no one knew who the father was. For some time the King was puzzled what to do, but in the end he sent the Princess to church with the child. The child was given a lemon to hold, and whomsoever he gave the fruit to should be deemed to be his father and the husband of the Princess. So it was arranged, and an order was given that only men of goodly appearance would be allowed to enter the church.

However, there lived in the town a little twisted hunchback who, being a simpleton, was called Simple Hans. Mingling with the crowd he made his way into the church unnoticed—and, when the child thrust out the lemon, it was to no other than Simple Hans! The Princess was taken aback, and as for the King he flew into such a passion that he had his daughter, the child and Simple Hans all thrown into a barrel and cast upon the waters.

The barrel soon drifted away, and when they were alone on the sea the Princess wept pitifully and cried, 'You horrid, impudent, hunchbacked monster, *you* are the cause of all my woe! Why did you push yourself into the church?—you have nothing to do with my child!'

'O yes I have,' replied Simple Hans; 'in fact I have quite a lot to do with it; for once I wished that you might have a child—and what I wish always comes to pass!'

'If that is so, wish us something to eat here and now.'

'That I can,' said Simple Hans, and wished for a bowl heaped with boiled potatoes. The Princess would have liked something better, but as she was very hungry she helped him to eat them. When they had eaten their fill, Simple Hans said, 'And now I'll wish for a good ship for us.' He had hardly uttered these words when they were in a splendid ship, and everything they could wish for was there in plenty.

The helmsman steered straight for the shore, and, when they landed, Simple Hans exclaimed, 'Now we want a castle here.' And lo and behold! there stood a fine castle; and servants in gold livery came and escorted the Princess and her child inside. As they reached the Great Hall, Simple Hans cried, 'Now I wish to be a smart young Prince.' Instantly his hunched back vanished, and he was tall, straight and handsome. He found favour with the Princess, she married him, and they lived happily together for many years.

One day the old King, while out riding, lost his way and

chanced to come on the castle, which he was puzzled to see, as he had not noticed it before. When he appeared the Princess at once recognised him, but he did not know who she was, as he thought his daughter had perished in the sea long, long ago.

She entertained him richly, but when he made ready to go she secretly stowed a golden beaker in his pocket. After he had gone, she sent horsemen to stop and search him to find whether he had stolen the golden beaker; and, when they found it on his person, they took him back with them. He swore solemnly to the Princess that he had not stolen it; nor did he know by what means it had got into his pocket.

'That shows one must not judge by appearances,' she said, then made herself known as his daughter.

The King was overjoyed, and they all lived happily together till his death. Then Simple Hans became King.

THE LOVELY FLORANDINE

THERE was once a King whose Queen had died, and there was no one left to him save a son, who had not turned out well and had caused the King much sorrow. One day the King sat in his chamber fretting, when someone knocked at the door. On going to see who was there he found a little boy, who wept bitterly, saying that as his father and mother were dead he had no one to care for him. As this brought to the King's mind how sadly things had gone with himself, he took pity on the boy and kept him at the castle. He called him Prince Frederick, while his own son was Prince Charles.

The King put much more trust in his foster-son than he did in his own, so once when he had to go away, at parting he gave all the keys to Frederick, telling him that during the royal absence he might like to while away the time with his brother seeing over the castle. There was only one room he must not unlock.

Now when the King had gone, the two Princes went all round gazing at the treasures in the many rooms; but one door Frederick always passed over. Then the other boy pestered him, demanding why he didn't open that door, until Frederick at last confessed that the King had forbidden him to unlock it on pain of death. When the other Prince heard this, he became the more curious and would not leave Frederick in peace until he gave in and unlocked the door.

The room was quite empty except that on the farther wall hung a green curtain. Charles hastened over to that side, pulled the curtain away—and lo, there hung the portrait of a most beautiful Princess, with the inscription, 'The Lovely Florandine.' At once both Princes fell in love with the picture. Charles, however, chanced to touch it with his finger, making a dark smudge. In a panic they tried to rub it off, but the more they rubbed the bigger it grew, until soon the whole picture was smudged.

Then, very upset, they left the room, but hardly had they done so when the King came back, and saw directly from their anxious faces that something was wrong. He at once asked for the return of the keys, and went to look in the forbidden room. When he saw the picture all blotted out, he burst into a rage, saying that, since they had robbed him of the picture, they must now bring him the Princess herself. As the Princess was kept in a castle under a spell, they must first break this and then bring her to him, or he never wanted to set eyes on them again.

So the two went off and travelled a great distance, till at length they came to a vast forest through which they marched from morning to night without ever meeting a soul. They were about to give up and sleep under a tree when suddenly in front of them they saw a mighty castle. Over the gate was written, 'Lodgings for Prince Charles and Prince Frederick,' so they went in, but could not find anyone. They pressed through room after room, and at length came to one with a notice telling them to sleep there—and, sure enough, they saw two beds in the room, one inscribed 'For Prince Charles' and the other 'For Prince Frederick.' As they were both very tired they lay down on the beds, and Prince Charles fell sound asleep.

But Prince Frederick kept turning things over in his mind and could not get to sleep. He lay awake till the clock struck eleven, and then the door suddenly opened and a ghostly figure entered and walked towards the other bed. 'Prince Charles,' it said, 'I can tell you how to free the lovely Florandine.' Then, as Prince Charles was fast asleep, the ghost moved over to Prince Frederick's bed and spoke the same words; but he kept silent, knowing that it doesn't do to answer ghosts. When the ghost had said the words to each boy thrice, it left the room and began moaning and shrieking horribly outside the door. A second ghost, outside, asked why it went on like that. 'Because I wished to tell the two Princes the way to free the lovely Florandine, but neither would answer.' But the other ghost told the first to speak all the same, as perhaps the Princes might be listening.

So the first ghost said, 'He who will free the lovely Florandine must go down to the cellar in the early morning, at seven. He will find seven cellars side by side, each with wild beasts in it, bears in one, wolves in another, lions and tigers, one kind in each cellar, with poisonous plants between them. In the last, next to the Princess, lies a huge dragon with seven heads. Now at seven all the beasts sleep for three minutes, and before these are over he who will free the Princess must hasten through all the cellars—careful not to step on a snake—cut off the dragon's seven heads, and carry the Princess back the way he came.'

The second ghost now went into the room and spoke the same words as the first; but Charles was still asleep and Frederick kept silent. So the second ghost left the room and began lamenting like the first. Still a third ghost came, and the same thing happened. Prince Frederick, who had kept silent all the time, now knew exactly what to do. The ghosts meantime went on howling outside the door till the clock struck twelve, when of a sudden everything was quiet again.

All night Prince Frederick kept awake, and just before seven he got up and went down to the cellar. As the clock struck the hour the doors opened wide by themselves and the Prince hurried through the wild beasts without stepping on a single snake. In the seventh cellar he drew his sword and cut off the dragon's seven heads. Then he lifted the Princess in his arms and carried her back. He had just got out of the last cellar when —clang! the door closed and all the beasts awoke with a fearful roar. But he carried the Princess safely through and laid her down on the bed as she seemed in a faint.

At this the other Prince awoke, having slept on till then, and felt jealous that his brother had done all there was to do; but he said nothing, and, when the Princess came to, they all returned to the King's Court. Prince Charles then said to Frederick, 'As I am the King's true son, it is only right that I should go up to my Father first,' and taking the Princess by the hand he went up to the King, claiming that it was he who had freed her.

The King rejoiced at this, but asked, 'Where is your brother?' for he was surprised that it wasn't Prince Frederick who had carried out the task, and he wished to see him as well. So Frederick went up, and the King asked, 'Who freed the lovely Florandine?' Prince Frederick answered, 'I did, Your Majesty.' But when the other Prince denied this, he kept silent.

The King then bade them fight a duel so that the truth should be brought to light. But when they drew their swords, Prince Charles's was all white whereas Prince Frederick's was still stained with the dragon's blood. The King now knew that his son had tried to deceive him, and was minded to banish him from the land for ever. But Prince Frederick begged that he might stay, to which the King at length agreed.

But Prince Frederick ruled over the kingdom, and had the lovely Florandine as his Queen.

MASTER EVER READY

MASTER EVER READY had long been a soldier, but now the war was over there was nothing to do but the same old duties day after day; so he took leave of the army and resolved to get a place as footman to some noble gentleman. A footman got a uniform trimmed with gold and had plenty to do; besides there was always something new going on.

So he set out and came to a foreign Court, where he saw a nobleman taking the air in a garden. Master Ever Ready was not the fellow to hang back, but walked briskly up to him and said, 'My Lord, I wish to take service with a great gentleman. If you chanced to be His Majesty, that would suit me down to the ground. All that needs to be known I know—in short I can do whatever I'm told.'

'Right, my son, that suits me,' answered the gentleman. 'But first, tell me what I am wishing for at this moment.' Without making answer, Master Ever Ready turned about and dashed off to fetch a pipe and tobacco.

'Right, my son, you can be my servant, and I shall set you the task of getting the Princess Nomini, the fairest lady in the world, for my wife.'

'Well,' replied Ever Ready, 'nothing could be easier, and Your Majesty shall soon have her. Just give me a coach and six, a coachman, footmen, lackeys, flunkeys, a·cook—a complete royal suite, in fact. As for myself, pray have me fitted out with princely garments, and tell everyone to obey me.'

Soon they set out. Master Servant sat in the coach, and away it rattled towards the royal Court where the beautiful Princess dwelt. First they drove along the highway, then across the fields, and soon came to a deep wood alive with thousands of birds whose voices rose deafeningly into the blue air.

'Halt! Halt!' called Ever Ready. 'Don't startle the birds—they are praising their Maker; and some day they may help me. Turn to the left!'

So the coachman had to turn and drive the party round the wood. Before long they came to a big field where some thousand million ravens were all loudly calling for food.

'Halt! Halt!' called Master Ever Ready. 'Unharness one of the front horses, lead it into the field and kill it, and the ravens will get their fill. For my sake they mustn't go hungry.'

When the ravens had eaten their food, the coach moved on, and they came to a lake where a fish was moaning, 'For goodness' sake, help me. There's nothing to eat in this hopeless swamp. Set me in running water and some day I'll do you a good turn.'

Even before the fish had finished speaking, Ever Ready called, 'Halt! Halt! Master Cook, lift it into your apron, and you, good coachman, drive to where there's running water.' Ever Ready got out himself, and when he put the fish into the water, it swished its tail with delight. Master Ever Ready then said, 'Now let the horses gallop, if we are to reach our goal tonight.'

When he came to the city where the King lived, he drove straight to the best inn. The innkeeper and all his staff came out and gave him the warmest of welcomes for they thought a King from afar had come—though in fact he was but a servant! Ever Ready promptly had himself announced at the royal Court, did his best to win the King's favour, and asked the Princess's hand in marriage for his master.

'My son,' replied the King, 'many others have asked and have been refused, as none could perform the tasks I set them to win my daughter.'

'Well,' said Ever Ready, 'I beg Your Majesty to set me the tasks.'

Said the King, 'A quart of poppy seeds have been sown by my order. If you fetch them here, with not a single grain missing, I shall give you the Princess for your master.'

'Ha/Ha!' said Ever Ready to himself, 'why, that's child's play!'

He took a measure, a sack and some snow/white sheets, then went out and spread the sheets next to the sown field. Soon appeared the birds who hadn't been disturbed in their singing in the wood, and lifted the seeds grain by grain, then dropped them on to the white sheets. When they had picked up every single one, Ever Ready poured the seeds into the sack, tucked the measure under his arm and went to the King. He measured out the seeds, and thought that now the Princess would surely be given him—but in this he was mistaken.

'Just one other thing, my son,' said the King. 'One day my daughter lost her gold ring. That, too, you must find for me before you can have her.'

Still, Ever Ready was not daunted in the least, but said, 'If Your Majesty will kindly have the water and the bridge pointed out to me where the ring was lost, it will soon be returned.'

Reaching the spot he looked down and there swam the fish he had put into running water during his journey. The fish lifted its head, saying, 'Just wait a moment while I go down and fetch it for you—a whale has the ring under its fin.' And it soon came up again and threw the ring on to the bank.

Ever Ready took it to the King, but he only answered, 'Now, one last thing. In the wood lives a unicorn that has caused great havoc. Kill it, and there'll be no further task to perform.'

Once more Ever Ready took things coolly, and made straight for the wood. There were the ravens he had fed, and they said, 'Patience for a while. At the moment the unicorn lies sleeping, but not on its blind side. When it turns over, we'll peck out its good eye, then it will be quite blind and will run against the trees in its rage and brain itself. You can easily kill it then.'

Before long the animal rolled over this way and that in its sleep, and then lay on its other side, whereupon a raven flew down and pecked out its good eye. Smarting with pain, the unicorn sprang up and dashed madly around in the wood, till soon it ran headlong into a stout oak. Ever Ready leapt forward, cut off its head and carried it to the King.

At this the King could no longer refuse his daughter, but entrusted her to Ever Ready, who, with all the pomp of the outward journey, seated himself beside her in the coach and drove off to his master to bring him his loving bride. He was welcomed with open arms, and the wedding was a right royal one. Ever Ready himself became the King's First Minister of State.

Whenever this story has been told, all have wanted to join in the party—one as a lady's maid, another as a sewing-maid, others as the footman, the cook, and all the rest of the good folk.

PRINCESS MOUSE-SKIN

A KING had three daughters. As he was anxious to know which of them loved him best, he called them before him and questioned them. The eldest said that she loved him better than his whole kingdom; the second that she loved him more than all the precious stones and pearls in the world; while the third only said she loved him better than salt.

The King, enraged to hear his youngest daughter liken her love to such a trifle, gave her over to a servant with orders to take her to the wood and kill her.

When they got there, the Princess pleaded for her life. But the faithful servant would never have killed her anyway. He begged that he might go with her and be at her command. All she asked him to do was to bring her a cloak made of mouse-skin; and when he had fetched it, she wrapped it round herself, and went away.

She made straight for a royal Court near by, gave herself out as a man, and asked the King to take her into his service. When the King consented, she begged to be his personal attendant. Each night it was her duty to pull off his boots. He always flung them at her head; so, once when he asked her where she came from, she replied, 'From a country where they don't throw their boots at people's heads.' This made the King take notice of her.

One day the other servants, showing him a ring that Mouse-skin had lost, said it was so precious that 'he' must certainly have stolen it. So the King called Mouse-skin before him and asked where she had got it. At this, Mouse-skin, feeling she could keep her secret no longer, unwrapped the mouse-skin, let her golden hair fall loose, and stepped forth looking so beautiful, so very beautiful, that the King at once took the crown from his head, placed it on hers and declared her his wife.

Mouse-skin's father was among those invited to the wedding; but as he thought his daughter long since dead, he did not recognise her. When he found that all the dishes served him at table were unsalted, he lost his temper and cried, 'I'd sooner die than eat such food!' But at these words the Queen replied, 'You would sooner die now than live without salt, but all the same you once ordered me to be killed because I said I loved you better than salt!'

Then the King knew her for his child, kissed her and asked her forgiveness. To have found her again gave him more delight than his whole kingdom or all the precious stones in the world.

THE OGRE

THERE was once a Queen who put her child out to sea in a golden cradle and left her to drift away. Yet the cradle did not sink, but floated till it came to an island where the people ate human flesh. As the cradle came tossing by, the wife of one of the cannibals chanced to be on the shore, and when she saw the child, a beautiful girl, she thought she would take her and bring her up to become her son's future wife. She found it very hard, however, to keep the child safely hidden from her husband. The old ogre, if he had once caught sight of her, would have eaten her up, blood, bones and all.

So when the girl grew up she was to marry the young ogre, but, as she couldn't bear the very sight of him, she wept the whole day long. Then, when she was sitting by the water's edge one day, a handsome young Prince came swimming by, who pleased her very much and was in turn pleased by her; and they promised to marry each other. Just then the old cannibal wife came up, and in a rage to see the young Prince with her son's bride-to-be, she seized hold of him and cried, 'You wait! You shall be roasted alive for my son's wedding!'

Now the young Prince, the girl, and the ogre's three children all slept in the same room, and it happened, when night came on, that the old ogre fancied some human flesh. So he said, 'Wife, I won't wait till the wedding; give me the Prince at once.' But the girl, hearing this through the wall, got up instantly, took off the crown that one of the ogre's children was wearing, and put it on the Prince's head. The old cannibal wife came in, and, as it was quite dark, she felt over their heads. The child without a crown she bore off to her husband, who devoured him straight away.

Meanwhile the girl, now very frightened, thought to herself, 'Once day breaks, everything will be found out and it will be all up with us'; and she stealthily rose and fetched out a seven-league boot, a magic wand, and a cake with a bean in it that could answer any question. Then she fled with the Prince; and, as they wore the magic boot, they covered a mile with every step. Every now and again she asked, 'Bean, are you still there?' and the bean answered, 'Yes, here I am; but make haste, because the old cannibal wife is after you in the other seven-league boot, the one you left behind!'

Then the girl, taking the magic wand, turned herself into a swan and the Prince into a pond for the swan. The cannibal wife overtook them and tried to lure the swan to the water's edge, but she failed and went back home sorely vexed, while the girl and the Prince continued their journey.

'Bean, are you still there?' asked the girl. 'Yes,' answered the bean, 'here I am; but the old woman is coming again, for the ogre has scolded her for getting tricked.'

Then the girl raised the wand and turned herself and the Prince into a cloud of dust that Mrs Ogre couldn't get through. So the cannibal wife had again to return without success; and the others went on their way.

'Bean, are you still there?' 'Yes, here I am; but Mrs Ogre is coming once more—and she is taking mighty strides!'

For the third time the girl raised the magic wand, turning herself now into a rose-bush and the Prince into a bee. Then up came the old cannibal wife, who again did not recognise them in their new guise and had to go back home defeated. But this time the pair couldn't recover their human shape, because, in a panic, the girl had thrown the wand too far away. However, by now they had walked a great distance and the rose-bush was standing in a garden belonging to the girl's mother. The bee rested on the rose, and could sting anyone trying to pluck it.

Then it chanced one day that the Queen herself, on going into the garden, saw the lovely flower, and was so delighted that she tried to pull it off. Up buzzed the little bee and stung her in the hand so hard that she had to let go, though not before she

48

had wrenched the rose a little.

When she saw blood flow from the stalk, she commanded a fairy to come and break the spell on the flower. Then she at once recognised the girl as her own daughter, and her heart was filled with joy.

All was now prepared for a fine wedding, and many guests were invited. They came in their richest finery, a thousand lights shone in the Great Hall, and there was feasting and dancing till the small hours.

'Have you, too, been to the wedding?'

'Of course I was there. My bonnet was made of butter, but the sun shone and melted it away; my dress was a spider's web, but I walked through thorns and they tore it off; my slippers were of glass, but I stepped on a stone and they broke in two.'

THE CRAFTY WOLF

ONCE upon a time, on a chill winter's day, it happened that a wolf felt fearfully hungry. So he ran all about the wood till at last he came to a pool where the fishermen kept big barrels, to hold their catch taken at the ice-holes. As soon as the barrels were full, the fishermen carted them away; and the wolf, seeing his chance, ran after the carts, at a safe distance, in case any of the fish leapt out of the barrels, which were open at the top. In time so many fish did leap out that the wolf was able to get all he wanted, and more. So he took some away with him into the wood, and there he fell in with the fox.

When the fox saw the fine fish, he said, 'Ah, good-day, my dear wolf. Now where did you get these grand fish? I'm dreadfully hungry; you might be so kind as to tell me how you lighted on them; then I can get some too.'

'I caught them in the big pool. You just go there, poke your tail in the water, wait a bit, and lots of fish will cling to it. Then you can pick off all you want.'

The fox, thinking this quite simple, thanked the wolf and quickly ran to the pool. He thrust his tail into the water, and thought he would wait a good long while to get a really big haul; and it was nearly an hour before he at last decided to pull his tail up again. Alas! it was so solidly frozen into the ice that he simply could not move it! The fox bit and scratched furiously, but it availed nothing. Suddenly the fishermen appeared, come to catch more fish, and of course they saw the fox frozen in the ice. So they picked up their heaviest cudgels and beat him right and left on his red coat. Such a thrashing did they give him that in the end, to get away at all, he had to leave his tail behind.

Half dead, he struggled on till he met the wolf in the wood. 'What a sight you look!' cried the wolf.

'Well, I'd sat by the water for no time at all when my tail was frozen stiff; and when I tried to get away, the fishermen came and gave me such a beating that I had to leave my tail and run for it, with my coat almost torn off. I was lucky to escape with my life!'

'You'd waited too long,' replied the wolf; 'you should have been content with a smaller catch.'

Then they parted, the wolf grinning to himself, heartily pleased that for once the saucy fox had caught it.

THE WOODEN HORSE

ONCE upon a time there was a King and every year, on his Saint's Day, strolling players came from far and wide to entertain him with their tricks. The one who did best received a present of money from the King.

On one such day a lad came leading a wooden horse. 'Bid me ride anywhere at all,' cried he to the King, 'and I'll be here again within the hour.' As his horse was made of wood, every^ body laughed; but the King himself wanted to see how far the lad could go, and ordered him to fetch something from a town a twelve^hours ride off. So the lad climbed on his horse, and instantly was whisked up high into the air, to the amazement of the people who stood staring below. Then, lo and behold! before the hour was over, he shot down again from the sky, bringing back to the King what he had asked for from the distant town. At this the King exclaimed, 'You have done the best trick, and for that you shall be rewarded. So come with me to the castle.' And the lad went with him.

Meantime the King's son had taken a fancy to mount the horse, which had been left in the castle yard. But the wooden horse would not budge. Annoyed at this, he tried every means he could think of to make the horse go, till in the end he noticed a little screw, gave it a turn and at once rose high into the air. The trouble was—he couldn't stop again! All the crowd, with the old King and the young lad, shouted and shrieked their heads off, but without the slightest effect. The Prince worked away at the screw, however, and at last, happening to give it the right twist, he directed the horse downwards—but landed on the top of a tower in a strange and distant land. As he was hungry after his flight, the Prince began looking round the tower for something to eat.

Going down a stairway he came to a room where a most lovely girl was seated. She was startled at seeing a stranger, but he said, 'Don't be afraid, fair maiden, all I want is some food; I am human like yourself.' She gave him food, and he told her the story of how he had got there. Then she invited him to come again, so he went back the second night. The third night when he went to her, she came with him, mounted the horse and away they flew through the air.

They had flown for some time when they came down on a green meadow beside a wood. The Prince, who was tired, soon fell asleep, but the girl kept awake and the wooden horse stood stock-still by their side. Then twelve robbers came out of the wood and carried off the girl and the horse. She didn't dare cry out, as the robbers would have killed her; so when the Prince woke, it was to find himself all alone. He wept bitterly for the girl and his horse, thinking she had mounted it and flown away from him.

At last he decided to search for her, but, when he got to the wood, he was caught by other robbers and carried off to serve a master in a distant town. There he heard that a lovely maiden and a wooden horse had been stolen by the heathen and brought to that very town, which was in the heathen land. 'That must be the girl herself and my horse,' thought the Prince, and he resolved to save her.

Meanwhile the girl was kept a prisoner in a great castle, and the horse was tethered in the yard. The Prince found his way to the castle, took service with the heathen folk, and pleased them so much that at last they made him servant to the girl. When he saw her he at once knew her, though she did not recognise him. At length he showed himself to her, and they planned to escape from the heathen folk with the help of their horse. The heathens kept asking the girl questions about the horse, but she remained silent. Then the servant said to them, 'If you like, I'll show you the way to ride it; only, if I do, the lady must be mounted with me.'

To this the heathens agreed, but said he must on no account ride beyond the courtyard. He gave his word, but scarcely had he and the girl climbed on the horse's back when it swept clean up into the air, high over houses and hills. So away he went, with the heathen folk standing below and gazing after him.

The Prince and the girl reached his father's Court safely, where he married her. When the old King died, he left his Kingdom to the young Prince.

THE THREE SISTERS

THERE was once a rich King. So rich was he that he
believed his riches could never come to an end, and he
simply wasted them in foolishness—he played on a golden
board with silver skittles. Then one fine day it fell out that all
his great wealth was gone. So he had to pawn one town and
castle after another, till at last he had nothing left but one old
castle away in the woods. He betook himself there with the
Queen and the three Princesses, and led a miserable life with
scarce a thing to eat but potatoes, which appeared on the table
day after day.

Now the King thought he would go hunting and perhaps
bag a hare; so, stuffing his pouch with potatoes, he set forth.
But near by was a great forest no man ever dared enter, as
dreadful tales were told of what had happened to those who had
done so: bears had devoured them, eagles pecked out their eyes,
wolves, lions and other savage beasts lain in wait for them. But
the King was not afraid and went straight into the forest.

To begin with he saw nothing unusual; only the mighty
shapes of the trees, with all silent below. After tramping awhile,
he felt hungry, and sat down comfortably under a tree, ready to
eat his potatoes. Just then a bear shuffled out of a thicket,
shambled towards him and grunted, 'How dare you sit under
my honey-tree! You shall pay dearly for that.'

This gave the King such a fright that he handed his potatoes
to the bear to calm him down a little. But the bear just growled,
'Don't like your potatoes! I'd rather eat *you*! Nothing can save
you . . . unless, perhaps, you give me your eldest daughter. And
—if you do, I'll give you a hundred-weight of gold as well!'

The King, in dread of being eaten, answered, 'Yes, you can
have her—only do let me go!' At this the bear showed him the
way, growling after him, 'In seven days from now I'll fetch my
bride.'

But the King went home with an easy mind, thinking to himself the bear couldn't possibly squeeze through a key-hole, and certainly nothing else would be left open.

Once back at the castle, the King ordered all gates to be shut and draw-bridges to be raised. He bade his daughter be of good courage, and, to keep her quite safe from the bear-bridegroom, he gave her a small closet high up in the turret to hide in till the seven days were over.

However, on the seventh morning very early, when everyone was still asleep, a splendid carriage arrived at the castle, drawn by six horses and attended by many horsemen clad in gold livery. When it drew up, the draw-bridges lowered of their own accord and the locks sprang open without a key. Then the carriage drove on into the courtyard and a handsome young Prince stepped down. When the King, awakened by the clatter, looked out of his window, he saw the Prince fetch his eldest daughter out of the locked room and lift her into the carriage. He could only call after her:

'Adieu! Adieu! dear daughter fair!
Adieu! Adieu! Bride of the Bear!'

From the carriage his daughter waved to him with her little white handkerchief, then away they sped as if harnessed to the wind—straight into the magic wood!

But the King was heartbroken at having given his daughter to a bear; and, with the Queen, he wept for three whole days, so sad was he. But the fourth day, when he had wept enough, he felt that what was done could not be undone, and went down to the courtyard. There he found an ebony chest, terribly heavy to lift. Soon, recalling what the bear had promised, he opened it—and there lay a hundred-weight of gold, glittering and sparkling. At the sight of the gold the King felt comforted, and soon redeemed his towns and his realm. Then he wasted his riches on trifles as unwisely as before. This lasted as long as the hundred-weight of gold, when again he had to pawn every-thing, go back to the castle in the wood, and eat potatoes.

Now the King still had a falcon, which he took one day into the fields to hunt for something better to eat. But the falcon rose and flew towards the dark magic wood, which the King no longer dared enter.

The falcon had hardly got there when an eagle shot out of the wood and pursued it. It flew back to the King, who tried to ward off the eagle with his spear, but the bird snatched the spear from him and broke it like a reed. The eagle next crushed the falcon with one of his talons, while with the other he clawed the King's shoulder, crying, 'Why do you invade my kingdom of the air? For that you must die, unless you give me your second daughter as wife.' To this the King answered, 'Yes, you can have her; but what reward do I get?'

'Two hundred-weight of gold,' said the eagle; 'and in seven weeks I shall come and fetch her.'

Then the eagle let go of him and flew back to the wood.

The King was grieved to have sold his second daughter also to a wild beast, and dared not tell her what he had done. Six weeks passed by, and in the seventh the Princess went down to a lawn in front of the castle to sprinkle her linen with water—when suddenly a splendid train of handsome knights came riding up. The handsomest knight, who rode at the head, dis-mounted and cried,

> 'Mount quickly, mount quickly,
> O maiden so fair;
> Come with us, come with us,
> Eagle-bride of the Air.'

Before she could reply, he had lifted her on to his horse and was galloping off with her to the wood, like a bird.

'Adieu! Adieu!'

Long did they wait in the castle for the Princess, but never, never did she return.

At length the King confessed that one day, when in dire need, he had promised his daughter to an eagle; and the bird must have claimed her. Then, after his sorrow had passed off a little, the eagle's promise came back to his mind. Down he went to the courtyard, and on the lawn he found two golden eggs, each of a hundred-weight. A suitor who had so much gold was good enough for him, he thought, and quickly drove all grief from his mind.

The merry life began again, and lasted until the two hundred-weight of gold was spent. The King then returned to the castle in the woods, and the only Princess left had to boil the potatoes.

The King had no wish to hunt any more hares in the wood, or birds in the air; but he would dearly have liked some fish! So he bade the Princess make him a net. He went to a pond not far from the wood, and, finding a boat, he got into it and cast his net. In one haul he caught a great pile of fine red-spotted trout. But when he tried to drag the boat to land it stuck fast and simply would not move, do what he might.

Suddenly a huge whale came puffing along, and snorted, 'How dare you catch my subjects! It will cost you your life!' With that he opened wide his great jaws as if to swallow both King and boat. When the King beheld those dreadful jaws his heart sank. Then he remembered his third daughter, and cried, 'Spare my life, and you shall have my youngest daughter.'

'Very well,' snorted the whale, 'and I'll give you something in return, too. I haven't any gold—don't think much of it!—but the bottom of my lake is paved with pearls; and you shall have three bags full. In the seventh month I shall come and fetch my bride.' And he vanished beneath the water.

Then the King drifted ashore and took his trout home with him. But when they were fried, he couldn't bring himself to eat a single one! For when he looked on his daughter, the only one left and the fairest and dearest of them all, he felt as if a thousand knives were stabbing at his heart.

Six months passed like this, and the Queen and Princess could not make out what was wrong with him: not once had he looked the least bit happy. In the seventh, the Princess was standing one day in the courtyard, filling a glass of water at the fountain, when a carriage drew up with six white horses, and in it were silver-clad figures. A Prince got down from the carriage, so handsome that she had not seen a finer man in all her life. He asked for a glass of water. When she gave him the one she was holding in her hand, he threw his arms round her and lifted her into the carriage. Then out of the gate they went and across the fields to the pond.

'Adieu! Adieu! O maiden rare;
Adieu! Adieu! Whale-bride so fair!'

The Queen stood at her window and just caught sight of the carriage in the distance. When she could not find her daughter, her heart grew heavy, and she called and searched for her every-where—but nowhere was she to be heard or seen. Then she knew the truth and began to weep. The King now confessed that in all likelihood a whale had taken their daughter away; for he had been forced to promise her to the beast, and that was why he had been so unhappy all along. Hoping to comfort the Queen, he told her about the great riches they would be receiving in return. But the Queen would not listen to a word, saying that her only remaining child meant more to her than all the riches in the world.

Now while the Whale Prince was carrying off the Princess, his servants put three heavy sacks into the castle. The King found them standing by the door, and when he opened them, he saw they were crammed with beautiful large pearls the size of the biggest peas. So in a trice he was as rich as ever, or even

57

richer, and he redeemed his towns and castles. This time, however, he did not go back to his old life of wasteful folly, but remained sober and thrifty. For when he thought of how his three dear daughters might be faring with their wild beasts— who had perhaps already devoured them—he had no spirit left. Nor could the Queen be comforted: she wept more tears for her daughter than the pearls given for her by the whale.

Then bit by bit the sorrow eased, and indeed after a while the Queen quite brightened up when she gave birth to a fine boy. As the Lord had sent the child so unexpectedly, they called him Reinald, the Wonder Child. He grew tall and strong; and often the Queen would tell him about his three sisters and how they were held in thrall in the magic wood by the three animals.

When he was sixteen, the boy asked the King for a suit of armour and a sword. With these he was ready to set forth on his adventures. So he blessed his father and mother, and went off.

He took his way straight to the magic wood, with only one thought—to find his sisters. But for a long time he wandered about the forest without meeting man or beast; till, after three days, he caught sight of a young woman sitting before a cave. She was playing with a bear-cub, and another very young one was lying in her lap. Thinking, 'Surely that must be my eldest sister,' Reinald tethered his horse and walked up to her. 'Dearest Sister, I'm your brother Reinald, and I've come to visit you.'

The Princess gazed at him, and as he looked the image of her father, she did not doubt his words; but, almost frightened out of her wits, she cried, 'O dearest Brother, if you care anything for your life, flee from here as fast as you can. Should my husband, the Bear, come home and find you here, he will devour you without pity.'

But Reinald answered, 'I'm not afraid, and will not leave you before I hear all about you.'

When the Princess saw she could not persuade him, she led

him into the cave, which was dark and a real bear's den. On one side he saw a heap of leaves and straw where the old bear and his cubs slept, while on the other was a fine bed of red and gold cloth for the Princess. She bade Reinald hide under the bed, and handed him down some food.

A little later the bear came home. 'I smell, I smell the flesh of a man,' he growled and made as if to poke his big head under the bed. At that the Princess replied, 'Oh, do be quiet! whoever could get in here?'

'I came upon a horse in the wood and have made a meal of it,' grumbled the bear, the blood still dribbling from his jaws. 'With the horse goes a man—and I can smell him.' Again he made a move towards the bed, but the Princess landed him such a kick that he turned a somersault, then sidled to his bedding, thrust a paw into his mouth, and fell fast asleep.

Each seventh day the bear took on his natural shape and became a handsome Prince, while his cave changed into a fine castle and the beasts of the wood into his servants. It was on one such day that he had fetched the Princess. Charming girls had received her at the castle, there had been a lavish feast, and she had fallen off to sleep full of happiness. But when she had woken again, it had been to find herself in a gloomy bear's den with her husband turned back into a bear growling at her feet.

Only the bed and the things she had touched remained unchanged. So for six days she lived in misery, but on the seventh she was comforted; and as she was not growing old— for only the one day counted towards her age—she was not dis-contented with her life. She had borne her husband two Princes, who also were bears for six days, but took on human form on the seventh. Each such seventh day she used to stuff her bed-straw with the most tempting food, cakes and fruit, on which to live through the coming week. The bear was biddable, and did whatever she asked him.

Now when Reinald awoke, he was lying in a silken bed, and

servants came to attend him and clothe him in the richest robes, for the seventh day had just come round again. His sister, with the two comely Princes and his brother-in-law the bear, came in and were glad to see him. All was fair and noble, and the whole day passed in sweetness and joy.

But in the evening the Princess said, 'Dear Brother, make haste now to escape. At daybreak my husband will turn into a bear again, and, if he finds you here in the morning, he won't be able to help his nature, but will eat you.'

Just then the Bear Prince came up and gave him three hairs taken from a bear, with the words, 'When you are in need, rub these, and I'll come to your aid.'

They kissed each other good-bye, and Reinald climbed into a carriage drawn by six black horses and drove off. Up hill and down dale he went, up and down, through forests and desert places, hedges and thickets, without pause or rest till morning came; then the skies began to lighten—and Reinald found himself of a sudden lying on the ground. Carriage and horses had melted away, and in the dawn he saw six ants galloping off, drawing a nutshell.

As he was still in the magic wood, he thought he would go in search of his second sister. For three days he wandered about in the wilderness without success, but on the fourth he heard the beating of a great eagle's wings as it swept by to settle on its nest. So he hid in the bushes and waited for it to fly off again; and, sure enough, after seven hours it rose. He came out of hiding, stood under the tree and called, 'Dearest Sister, if you are up there, let me hear your voice. I am Reinald, your brother, and have come to visit you.'

Soon a voice called down, 'If you are Reinald, my dearest Brother, whom I have never seen, pray come up here to me.'

Reinald tried to climb up, but found the trunk too broad and slippery. Thrice he made the attempt and failed; when a silken ladder came down on which he mounted to the eagle's nest, which was firm and strong like a platform built on a lime-tree. His sister was sitting under a canopy of rose-coloured silk, and in her lap lay an eagle's egg which she was keeping warm for hatching. They kissed in greeting and were overjoyed; but after a little while the Princess said, 'Now, dearest Brother, make haste and leave again. If the Eagle, my husband, finds you, he will peck your eyes out and devour your heart—he has already done that to three of your servants who were out in the wood looking for you!'

'No,' answered Reinald, 'I am staying till your husband changes his shape.'

'That won't be for another six weeks; but, if you can put up with it, I'll hide you in the trunk of the tree, which is hollow, and will get food to you each day.'

Reinald squeezed inside the trunk, the Princess let food down to him daily, and, when the eagle flew off, he climbed out to her. Then after six weeks the change took place, and Reinald awoke in a bed—the same as at his bear brother-in-law's, except that now all was even more splendid. So for seven days he lived very happily with the Eagle Prince, but on the seventh night they bade each other farewell. The eagle gave him three eagle feathers and said, 'When you are in need, rub these, and I'll come to your aid;' then he told his servants to go with Reinald and show him the way.

Now when morning came the servants suddenly vanished, and Reinald found himself alone on a high and dreadful cliff. He looked about him and saw in the distance the shining surface of a great lake gleaming in the first rays of the sun. He thought of his third sister and how she would be down there, and at once started the descent, working his way bit by bit among bushes and rocks. This took him three whole days, and he often lost sight of the lake, but on the morning of the fourth he reached the shore, and called, 'Dearest Sister, if you are down there, pray let me hear your voice. I am Reinald, your Brother,

61

and have come to visit you.' But no one answered: all was still.

Next he scattered bread-crumbs on the water and said to the fishes, 'Dear fishes, please go down to my sister and tell her that Reinald the Wonder Child is here and wishes to see her.' But the red-spotted trout snatched at the crumbs without heeding his words.

Then he saw a boat, cast off his armour and, with no more than his glittering sword in his hand, jumped on board and rowed away. He had drifted for some time when he saw sticking out of the water a chimney made of rock-crystal, from which came a pleasant smell. He rowed towards it, thinking that surely it must be there his sister lived, climbed into the chimney, and went shooting down. The Princess started up in alarm at suddenly seeing a pair of legs swaying in the fireplace, but then the whole man appeared and made himself known as her brother.

She was delighted, but soon her face clouded over and she said, 'The Whale heard you were going to visit me, but feared that, if you came while he was a whale, he wouldn't be able to help swallowing you. He'd smash my crystal house, and I'd perish in the floods myself.'

'Can't you hide me till the spell is broken?'

'Impossible! How could I? Can't you see that all the walls are crystal-clear?'

However, she thought and she thought, till at last she remembered the room where they kept the firewood. She stacked the wood so close that nothing could be seen from the outside, then hid the Wonder Child safely. Soon after the whale came home, and the Princess trembled like an aspen leaf. He swam time after time round the crystal house, and, when he caught sight of part of Reinald's jacket peeping out from under the wood, he thrashed with his tail, gave a terrifying snort, and would have smashed the house had he seen more.

Every day he came and swam once round, but at length, in

the seventh month, the spell duly broke. Reinald then found himself in a castle surpassing even the eagle's in splendour. It stood in the middle of a fair island. There for a whole month he lived in sheer delight with his sister and brother-in-law. When the month was over the whale gave Reinald three scales and said, 'When you are in need, rub them, and I'll come to your aid.' Then he had Reinald taken to the shore, where he found his armour again.

For seven days the Wonder Child roamed through the wilderness, and for seven nights he slept under the stars. In the end he caught sight of a castle, which proved to have an iron gate with a huge lock to it. A black bull with glowing eyes guarded the entrance, and Reinald rushed on the beast and dealt it a fierce thrust in the neck; but, as this was made of steel, the sword splintered like glass. He next tried with his spear, and it broke like straw. The bull then tossed him in the air with its horns, and he landed in the branches of a tree. Now in dire need, he bethought him of the three hairs of the bear and rubbed them in his hand. On the instant a bear came shambling along, turned on the bull and rent it in pieces—when, lo and behold! a duck rose from the entrails and flew rapidly off.

Reinald next rubbed the three eagle feathers, and at once a mighty eagle swept through the air after the duck as it made straight for a lake, and swooping down upon it, seized and devoured it. But Reinald noticed that, a little before, the duck had dropped a golden egg into the water. So he rubbed the three scales in his hand, and at once a whale came swimming along, swallowed the egg, and spat it on to the land.

Reinald took it up and broke it open with a stone, to find inside a little key, the very key to open the iron gate. Indeed, when he just touched the lock with it, the gate sprang open by itself, and he entered. The bolts on the farther doors, too, shot back of their own accord, and through seven doors he entered seven noble rooms, all brightly lit, till in the last he saw a maiden lying on a bed asleep. So lovely was she that he was quite blinded by her beauty.

Reinald tried to waken her, but failed, for she slept as soundly as if she were dead. In a temper he hit a black board next to the bed, and that very moment the maiden awoke, only to fall asleep again the next. At this he picked up the board and flung it down on the stone floor so that it smashed into a thousand pieces.

Hardly had that happened when the maiden opened her eyes wide—the spell was broken. It chanced that she was the sister of Reinald's three brothers-in-law, and, as she had refused her love to a wicked wizard, he had put her into a death-like sleep and changed her brothers into beasts. The spell was to last as long as the black board remained unbroken.

Reinald now led the maiden into the open air, and when they were outside the gate his brothers-in-law came riding up from three sides, the spell on them broken, and on their wives and children too. The Eagle-bride, having hatched her egg out, carried a lovely baby girl in her arms.

All then went to the old King and Queen; and so the Wonder Child had brought his three sisters home. Shortly after, he married the beautiful maiden, and there was joy and happiness everywhere—and now:

> The cat runs Home—
> My Tale is done.

THE SHOEMAKER AND
THE TAILOR

HILL AND DALE can never meet, but men can; and so it happened that a shoemaker and a tailor once met at a crossroads. The tailor was a jolly little fellow, and, on seeing

the shoemaker come from the opposite turning, he recognised
his trade from the bag he carried and sang out the words:

> 'Sew, sew the seam,
> Draw, draw the thread,
> Knock the little tack in—
> All is said!'

But the shoemaker couldn't take a joke, and, pulling a long
face, he made as if to seize the tailor by the throat. Upon this
the tailor burst out laughing, saying that he hadn't meant any
harm; then he handed the shoemaker his flask. 'Well,' said the
shoemaker, taking a hearty swig, 'they talk too much about
hard drinking, and too little about the fearful thirst that causes
it. Now a friend like you I'd always want with me.' 'Nothing
easier,' replied the tailor, 'if you are making for the royal city too,
for then we're both going the same way.' The shoemaker said
he was, and they jogged along side by side, one foot before the
other, like a weasel in the snow.

The pair took quite a time, with scarce a morsel to put in
their mouths. When they came to a town, they went round
calling on the tradesmen, and as the tailor looked so bright and
merry, many a master's pretty daughter gave him a kiss behind
the door and something for his journey too. So at night, back
in their lodgings, he always had more than the surly shoemaker;
yet he shared with him all he had made, and when the shoemaker pulled a long face and grumbled, 'The bigger the rascal,
the bigger the luck,' the tailor just whistled and sang, thumped
on the table, and called for beer. 'Lightly come, lightly go' was
his way.

One day they came to a great forest with two paths through
it, both leading to the royal city, one a seven-days journey and
the other taking only two days. But nobody could tell which
was which. So they sat down under a green oak-tree and took
thought whether to carry bread enough for seven days or just for

two. 'Look before you leap, they say,' argued the shoemaker, 'and I'll take for seven days.' 'Why lug along so much bread?' urged the tailor; 'I trust in God, and trouble over naught. The money in my pocket is good both summer and winter, but bread soon goes stale and often enough mouldy too. No, I'll just take bread for two days—even a deer doesn't carry a tail longer than it has to.' So they bought the bread and set off through the forest.

Amongst the trees all was as quiet as in church—there wasn't a breath of wind, no water murmured, no bird sang, and the foliage was so thick that the whole day long not a ray of sunshine came through the branches. On the way the shoemaker uttered no word; but though all was so gloomy outside, in his heart the tailor was as merry as a cricket, and, when he didn't know what to do with himself, he broke out into whistling and singing, till the dear Lord in Heaven rejoiced to hear him.

For two days all went well, but on the third, when there was still no end to the forest, the tailor felt a little cast down, yet he still trusted in God and his luck. When night came on he lay down, hungry, under a tree, and in the morning he got up hungry again; and so it continued on the fourth day. All the time he had to look on while the shoemaker ate his meals, for, when he begged for a hunk of bread, the shoemaker only answered mockingly, 'You have always been so gay, you can now be glum for a change—birds that sing in the morning, the cats get at night!' He just let him look on, and had no pity.

Now on the fifth morning the poor tailor couldn't rise, he could scarcely speak, his cheeks were white and his eyes were red. The shoemaker at length said, 'Today I'll give you bread, but to make up for it, you shall lose your right eye.' As the poor tailor dearly wished to live, he couldn't help himself; so weeping a last tear from both his eyes, he stood ready, and the shoemaker gouged out his eye with a bread-knife. Then the tailor bethought himself of what his old mother had said when long ago she had caught him in the pantry, 'Eat what you can and take the punishment you must.' So, after eating his bread, he set off walking again and soon forgot his misfortune.

But on the sixth day his hunger returned and kept gnawing at him; and on the seventh morning, once more he could not rise, and death loomed near. Then the shoemaker said, 'Today I'll give you bread again, but I'll put out your other eye too.' At this the tailor was sorry for being gay and thoughtless, and, praying God to be forgiven, said to the shoemaker, 'Do so if you must; but remember that Our Lord does not judge us here and now, and some day He will pay you out, for you do an evil thing which I have not deserved of you. In my trade every stitch must be alike, and without my eyes I cannot sew any more and must go begging. Do with me what you must, I'll suffer what I have to; but don't leave me here alone or I shall perish miserably.'

Then the shoemaker took his knife and put out the other eye, till the blood ran like tears down the tailor's cheeks. The shoe-maker gave him some bread to eat, put a stick into his hand, and drew him along behind him.

That evening they got through the forest, and in front of them, just outside, stood the gallows. Here the shoemaker left the tailor lying, and went on his way. Weary, hungry and in pain, the tailor dozed off and slept the night through, little thinking he was under the gallows.

Next morning he heard the sound of two voices overhead: they came from the poor sinners hanging on the gallows. Said the one to the other, 'Brother, are you awake?' and the other replied, 'Yes, I'm awake.' 'Then I'll tell you something,' said the first; 'if blind men knew that the dew fallen on us this night from the gallows could give them back their eyesight, many who have given up all hope would be able to see.'

Now when the tailor heard this, he pulled his handkerchief from his pocket, drew it over the grass, and rubbed his eye-sockets with it. Before long he saw the sun rise behind the hills, and, as he went on rubbing, he could soon make out, on a distant slope, the splendid royal city with its hundred gates: he could see every tree, every bird and even the midges dancing in the air. Next he took a needle from his pocket, and found he could thread it as well as ever. Then his heart began to dance with joy, and falling on his knees he said his morning prayers, not forgetting to put in a word for the poor sinners swinging about in the wind like bell ropes. After that he picked up his bundle, threw it across his shoulder, and went on in his usual way, singing and whistling merrily.

The first thing he met was a little brown foal, which he caught by the mane, intending to mount him and ride to the city. But the foal pleaded with the tailor, saying, 'Please don't ride me, for I am still so young, even a merry little tailor like you would break my back. Let me go and enjoy myself while I can, and some day I'll do you a good turn.' The tailor, being a good hearted fellow, let the poor little thing trot away, giving him a touch on the hind quarters with his switch so that he kicked up his heels for joy and leapt away across hedges and ditches.

But once more our tailor had had nothing to eat since the day before, and, if the sun filled his eyes with light, it didn't fill his mouth with bread. So he said to himself, 'I shall eat the first thing that comes my way,' and the first thing coming along was a stork. He grabbed him by the legs and made ready to kill him, but the stork began begging for his life; and, as the stork is a holy bird, he let him go, and went on again with an empty stomach.

Next he came to a pond with young ducks swimming about. One of these he snatched, and was about to wring his neck when along came the mother duck and begged for her little one. As he hadn't the heart to kill the duckling, he put him back on the water and let him swim away.

The fourth thing he came to was a hollow tree, where bees had their hive and kept their honey. He was just going to have a lick when the queen bee rushed out and threatened him. If he touched the honey, she said, they would sting him till he was riddled with holes, but, if he went his way, they would do him a service when the time came.

'Three dishes empty, and nothing on the fourth' thought our tailor and leaving the honey alone he took to the road and came at noon to the city. He first sought beer and bread, and then looked for work; and, as he knew his trade well, he was made the Court tailor.

Now, that very day the shoemaker had been appointed Court shoemaker, and, when he saw the tailor and found he had his two eyes again and was the Court tailor, his conscience pricked him and he feared the tailor might do him harm. So he pondered how to get rid of him, and at dusk crossed the courtyard to the King and said, 'O Mighty King, the tailor has boasted that he will get back your crown, which was lost in your father's day.' The King then ordered the tailor to appear before him, and said, 'Get me back the crown that was lost in my Father's day, or in twenty-four hours you shall quit the city.' The tailor thought to himself, 'Only a rogue promises more than he has; and, if the surly old King wants that sort of tailor, he will just have to want, that's all. I don't need twenty-four hours to quit —I can leave this minute!' So he packed his bundle and went on his way. But once outside, he couldn't help feeling sad at leaving his fine position so soon; and he hung his head.

Before long he came to the pond where the duck lived, and the bird asked him what his trouble was; so he told the duck that he had been ordered to get back the golden crown. 'Oh, if it's only that,' said the duck, 'we can help you; for the crown fell into the water here. Now, just spread your handkerchief on the grass.' At once the duck dived under the water with the twelve ducklings, and in five minutes came up again sitting in

the middle of the crown, while the twelve young ones formed a ring all round their mother. Then they tugged the crown to the bank and drew it on to his handkerchief, where, as the sun's rays shone on it, it sparkled like a million precious stones. He knotted his handkerchief about the crown and bore it to the King, who was pleased to hang a heavy gold chain about the tailor's neck.

But the shoemaker went again to the King, and said, 'O Mighty King, the tailor has been boasting he will make a wax model of the entire castle, with all belonging to it—fixed and unfixed, inside and out—and so true that not a nail on the wall will be missing.' At this news, the King had the tailor up before him again, and ordered him to make a wax model of the entire castle, with all belonging to it—fixed and unfixed; and if he couldn't do it, or if one nail in the wall was missing, he should be shut up for life in a dungeon.

So the tailor went away again, and hung his head, not knowing what to do. But when he came to the hollow tree, the bees asked him if he suffered from a stiff neck, since his head was all awry; and when he had told his story, they buzzed round him saying, 'Go back home now, and return tomorrow at the same time. Mind you bring a sheet with you, and all will be well.'

So home he went, while the bees flew to the castle, and in at doors and windows, looking hard at everything inside and out. Then they made a wax model, and when the tailor came back to the hollow tree the next day, there was the castle—ready!— with not a nail missing in the wall or a tile on the roof; and all was as white as snow and smelt as sweet as honey. The tailor knotted it into his sheet and bore it off to the King, who stood the wax castle in his finest hall and in return gave him a large stone-built house.

Then the shoemaker went to the King for the third time, and said, 'O Mighty King, the tailor has heard tell that no water will spring in the castle yard, and has boasted that he could make a clear spring there.' So the King ordered the tailor to come before him once more, and said, 'By tomorrow morning you shall make a clear spring rise in the castle yard—or in that same yard the hangman shall take your life.'

Once more the tailor set out, and as it was now a matter of life and death the tears ran down his cheeks. But along came the foal, now a beautiful chestnut horse, and said to him, 'I know all about your trouble—just climb on my back and I'll help you.' At this the tailor swung himself on to the horse and rode back towards the town. Three times he rode round the castle yard, and, as he was making the third round, the horse fell and on the very spot the water spouted as high as a man on horseback and as clear as the blue sky. On seeing this the King clasped the tailor in his arms under the eyes of all the assembled folk.

It didn't take long before the shoemaker went to the King for the fourth time, saying, 'O Mighty King, the tailor has boasted he will get you a Crown Prince.' So the King ordered the tailor to come before him once again, and said, 'In nine days' time you must get me a Crown Prince, and then you shall marry my eldest daughter.'

Now the tailor thought this really too much, and weary of all the trouble he packed his bundle and left the town. Outside the gates he met the stork, who asked him why he was leaving the town so fast. 'Well,' answered he, 'I have to get the Queen a Crown Prince within nine days—and I can't do it.' 'But *I* can,' said the stork; 'just go to the Queen's bedroom on the ninth day, and I'll come to the window with the Crown Prince. When I knock you must let us in.'

So the tailor went to the King and said he would get the Crown Prince, but he must be by the Queen's bed-side on the ninth day.

When all had gone well and the Queen had got her chubby

Crown Prince, the tailor received the hand of the King's eldest daughter.

The wicked shoemaker was now ordered to leave the city; but, taking with him bread enough for only two days, and happening to pick the wrong path, he fell into a faint with hunger—and lies there to this very day.

THE RING AND THE LAMP

MANY years ago there was a magician who one day was looking for a lad to take on as his assistant. He came to a little house in a village, where a poor widow lived with her son, and asked the woman if she would hire out the lad to him, for which she would receive two bushels of corn and two silver crowns each month. As the lad would be looked after and she too would receive enough to live on, the mother agreed and the pact was made.

So the magician took the lad with him, and they went away into the forest and up into the hills, till they came at last to a deep, deep cavern. The magician told the lad to climb down into it, when he would find himself in a lofty room. He must not stay there, but move on to the second room, where again he mustn't linger, but open the door to the third. Whatever he discovered there he was to bring back to his master. The lad agreed and the magician helped him to climb down.

Once below, the lad saw he was in a bright and pleasant room, furnished with a table on which stood an old lamp. Round the lamp were many dishes holding roasts and cakes, and the lad fell promptly to and ate to his heart's content. The magician, growing impatient meanwhile, called angrily down into the cavern, and the lad at length moved on to the second room. But, when he opened the door, he stepped into a beautiful garden where there were richly-laden fruit-trees. The apples smiled at him so cheerfully that he started on them directly, and, having eaten his fill, lay down under a tree and fell asleep. He dreamt that a fair lady came up and spoke to him, then slipped a handsome ring on his finger. And, truly enough, on waking, he did feel a ring on his ring-finger; and he so much liked being in the garden that he was loath to leave it, for there all his wishes were fulfilled.

When he had stayed a good while in the beautiful garden he felt very lonely and dearly longed to return home and see what his poor mother was doing. At that moment the fair lady appeared again. He told her his wish, and she not only granted it, but made him a gift of the old lamp he had seen on the table; then she vanished. In less time than it takes to tell, he was back near his home and could see the village before his eyes. He dashed for his mother's cottage, greeted her joyfully, and told his story. In turn she told him that she had cruelly suffered while he was away. The magician hadn't given her any money or corn, and there was nothing left for her to live on.

After a day or two, as their need grew more and more pressing, they decided to sell the old lamp, even if they didn't get much for it. The lad took it, went with it to the little stream outside their door, and began polishing it up. While he was rubbing away at the ingrained rust, the fair lady suddenly appeared before him and asked him his wish.

'Oh,' he said, 'if only I had five crowns to get food for Mother and me!'

'Your wish has been granted,' she replied.

There, in his pocket, he felt the money. Happy again, he went into the house; and he stayed for some time with his mother. Then want returned, and again they decided to sell the old lamp. Once more he went to the little stream and began rubbing, and again the fair lady appeared asking him his wish. This time he wanted ten crowns; at once he felt them in his pocket, and ran back happily to his mother.

He knew now what a treasure he had in the lamp; and the third time he wished for thirty crowns, the fourth for a hundred. Then, as he grew ever more daring, he wished for fine clothes and precious things—and the fair lady granted all!

Nothing could equal the happiness of these poor people now. After they had enjoyed their luck for some time, the lad thought to himself, 'Of course, I've got fine clothes and pretty things, but it would be grand indeed if I also had a coach and a good pair of horses!' Hardly had he expressed his wish to the lady when the horses, complete with coach, stood outside the door.

So, with all this good fortune, he made up his mind to travel and see life. He said farewell to his mother, and drove off across the fields into the wide world.

One day he came to a noble castle, the seat of a very, very rich Count. This Count had arranged a great feast, to which he invited his richest and most important neighbours; and, as our lad wasn't thought of as one of the common folk, he too was asked. He took his place at table, everything shone and sparkled brightly, and he felt as happy as could be.

Then the Count announced the purpose of the feast: to give the wealthiest and mightiest man of those parts the hand of his fair daughter. The chosen man, however, must succeed in the task set forth on a little sheet of parchment, which was passed round the table. It said that only he should marry the fair Princess who in twenty-four hours could build a castle bigger and more splendid than the Count's! At this the guests shook their heads, for who would dare try for the fair Princess now?

But when the parchment came to the young guest, he remembered the lamp—which he had with him—and said to the Count, 'I will build a castle in twenty-four hours, more splendid than your own.' Then the Count, much astonished but very pleased, showed him the place to build on.

Now when everyone had gone to rest, a hammering and banging could be heard as of many thousand workmen; and this went on the whole night through. At daybreak the castle stood complete, facing the old one, and it was so splendid as far to outshine it. All the balustrades were of polished brass and richly gilded.

When the Count saw it he said with bated breath, 'You've kept your word; and I'll keep mine.' He gave the lad the fair Princess in marriage, and there was a wonderful wedding.

A few days later the Count took his son-in-law hunting with him, and was pleased to find how much the young man enjoyed the sport. They coursed the forest far and wide.

The fair Princess was alone meanwhile in the splendid castle; and while she was gazing out of a window, she saw a grimy old pedlar come to the gate. He was hawking fine, shining lamps, and these he offered to the Princess, who took a great fancy to them. Thinking they would make bright ornaments for the castle, she offered to buy them, but the hawker replied, 'Fairest Princess, I do not sell them, but I'll exchange them for old lamps.' 'I have an old lamp in the lumber-room, and I'll exchange that for yours,' the Princess said. So she fetched the old lamp down, and the hawker, only too pleased, took it. Instantly the great castle collapsed and disappeared, together with the Princess and all the treasures, so that not a trace was left.

When the rich Count with his son-in-law returned from hunting, to the merry sound of the hunting-horns, and saw that everything had vanished, with his dear daughter, he burst into a rage with the youth and called him a wicked sorcerer. He ordered a deep dungeon-hole to be dug and had his son-in-law thrown into it.

There the wretch lay in great misery and distress. He thought of his lamp, which he had left in the third room; and he wept for his beautiful wife, grieving till he looked as wan as a ghost. Now it chanced that, while he wrung his hands in sorrow, he turned the little ring, which still remained on his finger. At once the fair lady appeared, whose gift it was, and stood before him. He asked her help to escape from the hole, and, hey presto! he found himself free, and in beautiful open country. Then he turned the ring once more, the fair lady reappeared and he now asked her to restore his young wife to him—or he would certainly die. To this she replied, 'Go to Italy, and there you will find her with the wicked magician. He is disturbed about her, as she is ill with grief and sorrow. Give yourself out as a doctor; and you will cure her and get her back.' Then she vanished.

While weighing her words, he was already in Italy. He went to an inn, put on a gold-trimmed gown, and gave out that a famous doctor had arrived. Within a short time the magician asked him to call and make a sick lady well again and he would be richly rewarded.

The Princess, entering the room, was taken aback at sight of him, for, though sorrow had reduced him to a mere shadow of his old self, she recognised him at once.

'I will cure the young lady,' he said to the magician. 'But you must leave me alone in the room with her an hour each day for three days.'

The magician gladly agreed; and by the third day the patient was well again. The magician was delighted, and asked the 'doctor' his fee—even if he demanded a thousand crowns the magician would cheerfully pay it. The 'doctor' answered that he would like to be left alone with the young lady for just another hour, then he would tell him the reward he expected for the cure. The magician consented, drawing the girl aside to bid her promise whatever the doctor asked.

As soon as they were alone, the young 'doctor' locked the door and said to the Princess, 'The reward I ask is the old lamp you once exchanged—you know the one I mean.' 'Yes, I do,' the Princess answered. 'I'll go and fetch it—it's in the next room; a very old, rusty lamp.'

So she went and fetched it, the 'doctor' taking it from her with unbounded joy. On the instant the house and all within it disappeared, they were home again with the rich Count, and the splendid castle stood in its former place.

Great was the rejoicing then; and they lived happily for many years, guarding the lamp as their most precious treasure.

THE WORKER AND THE DRONE

THERE were once two journeymen who took the road together and bound themselves to stand by each other. But on reaching a big town, one of them took to evil ways, forgot his bond, left his friend, and went on by himself. He moved from place to place, preferring company that was noisy and gay. The other stayed out his time in the town, working hard, and at last moved on.

Then one night, unawares, he was passing by a gallows and saw a man lying asleep on the ground, clad in nothing but rags; and, as the stars shone brightly, he could see it was none other than his former mate. So he lay down beside him, covered him with his coat, and fell asleep.

However it was not long before he was wakened by the sound of two voices chattering together. These belonged to two ravens perched up high on the gallows. One said, 'The Lord will provide,' to which the other replied, 'But you also must do your bit.' Then the first one, quite worn out, fell to the ground; and the other stayed beside him and waited until daybreak, when he fetched worms and water, revived him, and thus saved him from death.

When the two journeymen saw this, they were astonished and asked the first raven why the other was so weak and ill. But the sick raven himself replied, 'Because I didn't want to bother myself, thinking Heaven would provide.'

The men took the ravens to the next town with them. On the way, the one was lively, searching for food, bathing each morning, and preening himself with his beak, while the other cowered in corners, was cross, and always had a bedraggled look.

Soon after, the daughter of the house where they stayed, a beautiful girl, became very fond of the lively raven. She picked him up, stroked him, and finally, pressing him against her face, kissed him for sheer delight. At this the raven dropped to the ground, rolled over, fluttered, and turned into a handsome youth.

He told her that the other raven was his brother. They had both offended their father, who had put a spell on them, saying, 'Fly about as ravens, until a beautiful girl kisses you of her own free will.' The one was now freed from the spell, but the other, the idle one, nobody wanted to kiss, and he lived and died as a raven.

This taught a lesson to Brother Looselife, who became hard-working and upright, and in future kept faith with his mate.

TWO BROTHERS IN FORTUNE

A FORESTER was once out shooting when in front of him came flying a beautiful bird, of a kind he had not seen before. Wishing to take it alive, he aimed with care, winged it, and it fell to the ground.

He carried the bird home to his wife, who shut it up in a cage. Three days later the forester was looking at the bird when he noticed it seemed distressed. This puzzled him and he asked his wife if perhaps she hadn't cleaned the cage out properly. She admitted that for two days she had forgotten to attend to it. They then examined the cage, and found a golden tablet inscribed with Hebrew letters. This he took to a Jew, who bought it for two hundred crowns.

Now the words inscribed on it said that whoever ate the bird's heart and lungs would become King; and whoever ate

the liver would find eleven pieces of gold beside him every morning. The Jew also bought the bird, for which he paid a hundred
and fifty crowns. His aim was to give one of his sons the heart
and lungs to eat, and the other the liver.

The Jew, a miserly fellow, would not eat the costly roast all
by himself but asked quite a crowd to the feast, including—for
the humour of it—the forester and his sons. When all were
gathered together fire broke out, and host, guests and servants
at once took flight—except the forester's sons. Instead they made
straight for the kitchen and the bird. The younger, seeing they
were alone, took a fork, scooped out the liver and ate it. He then
handed the fork to his brother, who scooped out the heart and
lungs and ate them likewise.

When the fire had been put out, the Jew and his company
returned and took their places at the table. The bird was brought
in, and the Jew started carving, eagerly probing for the liver,
lungs and heart; but, finding them gone, he was beside himself
with dismay and rage, and asked who had eaten anything out
of the bird. The forester's sons confessed; and their father was so
furious that he rushed them home and locked them in the cellar.

As the night wore on, with time heavy on their hands, the
younger one suggested they should try and squeeze through the
cellar grating and get away, and he himself promptly clambered
through. Once outside he called back to his brother, who was a
little bigger, 'Come on, dear Brother. Don't mind if the grating
hurts.' Then the older one followed and got out safely too.

They went to a friend of their father's and spent the rest of the
night at his house, getting up early next morning to go on their
way. Now, the friend, looking into the straw bedding, found
the eleven pieces of gold, and ran after the boys to restore the
money. 'No doubt your father sent you out for change, and
you've forgotten it,' he said. 'He did,' they answered and went
on their way merrily.

Every morning the younger boy found eleven pieces of gold

in his bed, till before long he was well off and bought himself a horse and carriage, and they both drove about far and wide. Soon they realised that they owed their luck to the bird's liver, and so they called themselves the Lords of the Bird.

At length they came to a great city where crowds of people were to be seen standing outside the gates. Asking what the matter was they were told that the Royal Princess was seeking a husband; she would release a white pigeon, and the man it settled on would become her spouse, and also King of the country. Curious to see what would happen, the boys stood amongst the crowd, and saw the Princess climb a steep hill with the ladies and gentlemen of the Court and set the pigeon free.

The bird flew quite a distance above the heads of many people, but finally settled on the head of the older boy. The younger had not seen this happen; and, as the crowd was mobbing his brother, the pair got separated. The gentlemen of the Court approached the elder boy and escorted him, beneath a canopy, to the castle, where he was immediately married to the Princess and proclaimed King.

The younger boy looked round a long while for his brother, and, when he couldn't find him, he went on his way sadly. At length, tired of wandering about alone, he took up his lodging at an apothecary's, as he wished to learn that trade. After a while, however, people whispered that there was something odd about his supply of money; and the apothecary's daughter made up her mind to get to the bottom of the mystery.

One Sunday afternoon she asked him to her room, and plied him with wine. The wine loosened his tongue and he gave away the whole secret. After that he was sick, and brought up the bird's liver, which the girl seized and greedily swallowed, so that from then onwards she found eleven gold pieces beside *her* every morning. As for the forester's son he became poorer and poorer. Then, unable to bear it any longer, he went out into the world again.

Before he had gone very far he came to a steep hill where nothing grew between the stones but fine little herbs, and, feeling fearfully hungry, he plucked a few and ate them. Hardly had he done so when he was changed into a donkey. At his wit's end to know what to do, he began to bray loudly, 'Hee-haw! Hee-haw!' A hermit who lived on the hill-top came down and said, 'What do you want, my son?' 'Hee-haw! Hee-haw!' 'Where do you come from?' 'Hee-haw! Hee-haw!' 'What's your name?' 'Hee-haw! Hee-haw!' When the donkey had replied three times, the hermit knew for sure that it was a man bound by a spell.

'Come with me, my son, and I'll help you,' he said, leading the donkey to his hut and giving him an apple. When the donkey had eaten it he regained his human form and told the hermit how the apothecary's daughter had tricked him out of his riches.

'My son,' said the hermit, 'we can make things right again if you'll do what I tell you. Take some of the little herbs—though not many—go back to the town, and stand at the church door on Sunday morning. She will come riding up in a coach and six, and, not recognising you, will say, "What have you there, my son?" You will reply, "The little herb of beauty." She will ask you to wait till she comes out, and then she'll take you to her room. Now give her the little herb to eat, get away at once, and come back here to me.'

Everything happened just as the hermit had foretold. On the Sunday morning the forester's son placed himself at the church door and the apothecary's daughter came driving up haughtily and said, 'What have you there, my son?' Hearing he had the little herb of beauty she was delighted, for since becoming rich she had keenly longed to be beautiful too—even more beautiful than the Royal Princess! After church she took him to her room and offered him many gold pieces; he gave her the little herb to eat—and she promptly changed into a donkey, that clattered down the stairs, braying loudly. The boy ran after it and out of the house. The apothecary's door stood open and the donkey trotted into the shop and broke everything there was in the place.

When the animal got tired with the romping, it climbed back to the room and crawled under the bed. The apothecary, dismayed to see all the damage, called for his daughter. They searched for her all over the house, and at last the donkey was hauled from under the bed. It seemed very sorry for itself; and the father realised that it must be his daughter transformed by some magic spell.

He had it given out through the land that all magicians and sorcerers should come to him, and whoever gave his daughter her human shape again would be richly rewarded. When this news reached the hill-top, the hermit gave the forester's boy an apple, telling him to give the apothecary's daughter a tiny piece each day and she would regain her human form bit by bit—only he should leave her the donkey's ears.

Setting off with the apple, the boy came to the city gate, where the guard asked him who he was. 'A magician above all magicians; a sorcerer above all sorcerers,' he answered.

Promising the apothecary to break the spell binding his daughter, he gave the girl each day a tiny piece of apple and then a sound thrashing. Without the thrashing the cure could not be effected, he told the father. At the point when she still retained the donkey's ears, the girl brought up the liver, which the boy at once swallowed. He then told the father that he could not remove the ears.

'Never mind,' remarked the apothecary, 'she can hide them under her bonnet.'

The boy received a rich reward, and went back to the hermit on the hill, who then showed him how to render himself invisible, and packed him off to the town where the older boy was King, reigning in peace and contentment. The younger boy went up to the castle, where, standing invisible near his brother at the dinner-table, he drank some of his wine and ate

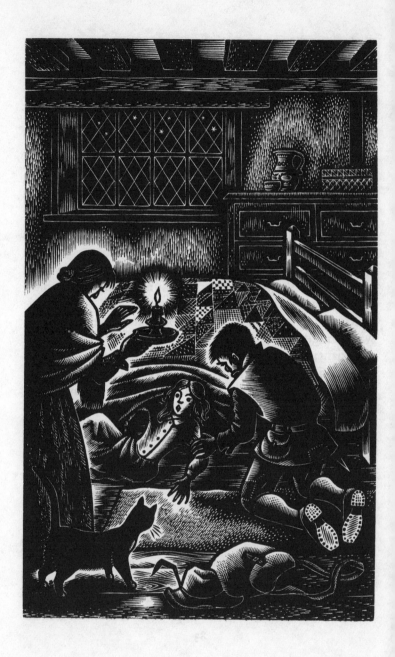

from his plate. The King grew alarmed. He felt someone was near, yet could not tell who it was. At times, when something was snatched away, he caught a glimpse of a hand; at other times he saw nothing. When he sat down for a smoke, his pipe was grabbed from him and smoked by invisible lips.

At last the King could endure it no longer. He ordered every inn-keeper to send all strangers to the castle. Now his younger brother was staying at an inn, and he sent his host to the King to say that he would not go—the King must come himself if he wanted to see him. At once the King came, and with delight recognised his dear brother, whom he had so much longed for.

Together they returned to the castle and lived happily for the rest of their lives.

PRINCE SWAN

ONCE upon a time there was a girl who lived in a great forest. One day a swan came walking up to her, carrying a ball of thread. He spoke to the girl, saying, 'I'm no swan, but an enchanted Prince; and you can break the spell if only you unwind the ball of thread—then I'll fly away on the end of it. But take care not to snap the thread or I shan't be able to reach my own kingdom and get free. If you unwind the whole ball, you shall be my bride.'

The girl took the ball, the swan rose into the air, and the thread unwound easily. The girl kept unwinding the ball all day, and by evening the end was in sight. Just then, unfortunately, the thread caught in a thorn-bush, and snapped.

Heart-broken, she began to cry. Then, as night fell and the wind howled through the trees, she took fright and began to run as fast as her legs would carry her. After a while she saw a faint light, and, making towards it, found a cottage and knocked at the door. An old wife came out, astonished to see a girl standing there.

'Well, my child, where have you come from so late?'

Said she, 'Please, please, give me shelter for the night—I'm lost in the forest. And please give me some bread to eat.'

'That's not so easy,' said the wife. 'I'd gladly give it to you, but my man eats human flesh and, if he finds you here, he'll have no mercy on you. Yet, if you stay outside, the wild beasts will eat you. So I'll see what I can do.'

Then she let the girl in, gave her a little bread, and hid her under the bed.

The man-eater always came home before midnight, when the sun had quite set, and went out again in the morning before the sun had risen. It wasn't long before he arrived.

'I spy, I spy the flesh of man!' he cried, and searched round the room. At last he felt with his hand under the bed and hauled the girl out. 'Here's a tasty morsel!' But the old wife begged and begged, till he promised to let the girl live that night, and not to eat her till breakfast next morning.

But before sunrise the old woman woke the girl. 'Hurry, hurry and get away before my man wakes. I'll give you a little gold spinning-wheel; and mind you guard it well! I am called Sun.'

The girl went on her way and in the evening came to a second cottage, where the same thing happened as the night before. And the second old wife, as she bade farewell, gave her a gold spindle, saying, 'I am called Moon.'

The third evening she came to a third cottage, and the old wife gave her a gold spool, saying, 'I am called Star. Prince Swan, though the thread was not fully unwound, had already gone far enough on his way to get back to his kingdom. There he is now King. He has married, and lives in great splendour on a glass mountain. You will reach it tonight, but a dragon and a lion are there to guard him; you must take this bread and bacon with you to calm them down.'

The girl did so, and throwing the bread and bacon into the monsters' mouths, they allowed her to pass—as far as the castle gate. Into the castle, however, they would not let her go.

So she sat down at the gate and began spinning with her little gold wheel. The Queen, watching from above, took a fancy to the pretty wheel, and she went down to ask for it. The girl promised it to her if she would allow her to stay a night in the chamber next to the King's bedroom. The Queen agreed, and the girl was taken upstairs. Every word spoken in the chamber could be heard in the bedroom.

Now, when night came and the King was in bed, she sang:

'Does King Swan not remember
His betrothed bride Julian?
Who passed by Sun, Moon, Star,
By Lion and by Dragon:
Will King Swan not awaken?'

But the King did not hear the words, for the cunning Queen, fearing the girl, had given him a sleeping potion and he slept so soundly that he would not have heard a note if she had sung to his very face.

In the morning all seemed lost, and she had to go outside the gate again. There she sat and spun with her spindle. This, too, drew the fancy of the Queen, and the girl gave it her on the same condition—that she might stay one night next to the King's bedroom. Again she sang:

'Does King Swan not remember
His betrothed bride Julian?
Who passed by Sun, Moon, Star,
By Lion and by Dragon:
Will King Swan not awaken?'

But the King again slept soundly from a sleeping potion; and now the girl had lost her spindle too.

So on the third morning she sat down at the gate winding her golden spool. The Queen fancied that treasure, too, and promised the girl that as reward she should spend another night next to the King's bedroom. But the girl, seeing how she had been tricked, asked the King's servant to hand him a different drink that night. Once more she sang:

> 'Does King Swan not remember
> His betrothed bride Julian?
> Who passed by Sun, Moon, Star,
> By Lion and by Dragon:
> Will King Swan not awaken?'

This time, hearing her voice, the King awoke, knew who she was, and said to the Queen, 'If you lose a key and then find it again, do you keep the old one or the new-made one?' 'Most certainly the old one,' replied the Queen.

'Well, then, you can no longer be my wife, for I've found my first betrothed again.'

Next morning the Queen was sent home to her father, and the King married his true bride. They lived happily together to the end of their days.

THE DEVIL AND THE
THREE SOLDIERS

THREE SOLDIERS, fleeing from the enemy, came to a pear-tree and one, in desperation, cried, 'The Devil take us!' The same moment a demon appeared, who made a pact with the soldiers to help them in their need. They had then to remain in Hell for a year, when the Devil would set them a riddle; but they were allowed out now and again for a walk.

Lucifer—who always stays at home himself, only packing off the demons to do his work—was far from happy, however, thinking, 'The demon may not set these fellows really hard riddles, and they'll get the better of him.'

One day the three soldiers were taking a stroll, and feeling depressed—especially the two who hadn't themselves called on the Devil. They blamed the other for the unlucky words he had spoken, which had brought this misfortune on them. 'You had better set to and help us, or it will be the worse for you!' they said to him.

'Anyway,' he answered, 'of the three riddles we'll surely guess one,' and he went off by himself to think about it. Coming to a tall pear-tree he climbed to the top and looked out over the country below. Just then he noticed Lucifer and a demon, also out for a walk, taking a seat under the pear-tree to have a rest.

'Listen,' said Lucifer, 'what sort of riddles have you thought of? I'm half afraid they'll guess them—old soldiers are devilish smart.'

'You can rest assured,' answered the demon, 'they'll never guess these. First, I'll give them a goatskin, but change it into Flemish cloth; second, I'll come riding on a billy-goat that will seem to them a magnificent horse; and third, I'll show them a drinking-cup made of pitch, which they will take for the most perfect gold cup.'

'Now all's well,' thought the fellow on the tree-top; but to the others he said not a word.

On the day appointed, the demon rode up, two of the soldiers were taken in by him, but the third one told him straight to his face, 'Your Flemish cloth is a stinking goatskin, your horse is an old billy-goat—good for you but no use to us!—and your gold drinking-cup is an old pitch-bucket, nothing more. I demand a pension from you for the rest of my days.'

So the demon, mad with rage, had to grant it, and carry all

the money they wanted to the spot where they had first made their pact.

THE MUSICIANS ON THE GALLOWS

THREE MUSICIANS once played at a big wedding that went on for three days before they could go home; and then it was late at night. On the way they met a coach filled with ladies and gentlemen who greeted them, saying, 'Good evening, musicians! Come and play for us: we are holding a great feast, and will give you all the money you ask for.'

'No,' answered their master, 'it can't be done—we've already played for three days and three nights, and we are dead tired.'

But the lads let themselves be talked round: they got into the coach, sped through the air like lightning, and came to a large castle. Assembled there were about a hundred folk all enjoying a good time and drinking wine from golden beakers; and they danced till the early hours of the morning.

Now, as the musicians' fiddles were old, the gentlemen gave them new ones to try, which they liked so much that they played a fine flourish on them. They then got their pockets stuffed with silver pieces, and were led to a large room with four-poster beds all ready for them. They hung their clothes in a wardrobe, and fell asleep.

But next morning, when they awoke, they were lying on the gallows next to a poor sinner, and their clothes hung on the cross-bar, their money was all cow-dung, their fiddles were old blocks of wood, and their golden beakers were cows' feet!

In fact they were as rich as they had been before the wedding, and they had lost their fiddles!

HURLEBURLEBUTZ

ONCE upon a time a King, while out hunting, lost his way. Suddenly a white manikin stood before him and said, 'Your Gracious Majesty, give me your youngest daughter and I'll show you the way out of the wood.' In desperation, the King agreed; and so the manikin set him on the right path. Then, as he bade farewell, he called out after the King, 'In a week's time I'll come and fetch my bride!'

But home again the King felt unhappy about his promise, for it was his youngest daughter that he loved the best. Soon the Princesses, guessing that something was wrong, pressed him to tell them his trouble, till at last he was driven to confess he had promised the youngest Princess to a white manikin in the wood, who would be coming to take her at the end of a week. When the Princesses heard this, they told him not to lose heart, for they would be more than a match for the manikin.

Then, when the day came, they decked out the daughter of a cow-herd in their finery, and told her to sit in their room. 'Remember,' they commanded, 'if anybody comes to fetch you, you must go with him.' The Princesses, however, left the castle.

Hardly were they gone when a fox came and said to the girl, 'Sit down on my bushy tail: Hurleburlebutz, away to the wood!' The girl sat down on the fox's tail, and was whisked off to the wood. They came to a bright green glade, where the sun shone clear and warm, and there the fox said, 'Get down now, and pick the lice off my coat.' The girl did as she was told, and the fox put his head in her lap as she picked away. While she was busy, the girl exclaimed, 'It was far nicer in the wood this time yesterday!' 'How came you to be in the wood?' asked the fox. 'Well, I was minding the cows with my father.' 'Then you are not the Princess! Sit down on my bushy tail: Hurleburlebutz, back to the castle!'

The fox carried her back again, and said to the King, 'You

have deceived me! That girl's a cow-herd's daughter. I'll return in a week's time and fetch your own child.'

On the eighth day, however, the Princesses dressed a goose-herd's daughter in fine clothes, told her to sit, and went away. The fox came as before and said, 'Sit down on my bushy tail: Hurleburlebutz, away to the wood!' When they came to the sunny glade the fox again said, 'Now get down and pick the lice off my coat.' While she was busy, the girl sighed and exclaimed, 'I wonder where my geese are now!' 'What do you know about geese?' 'Well, I tend them every day on the green with my father.' 'So you are not the King's daughter! Sit down on my bushy tail:Hurleburlebutz, back to the castle!' When he had carried her back, he said to the King, 'You have deceived me again—the girl is a goose-herd's daughter. I shall come back once more, in a week's time, and if you don't give me your daughter then, you shall pay dearly for it.'

The King was now really alarmed, and when the fox came back he gave him the Princess.

'Sit down on my bushy tail: Hurleburlebutz, away to the wood!' Then she had to ride away on the fox's brush, and when they came to the sunny glade he said to her, 'Now get down, and pick the lice off my coat.' But when he put his head in her lap, the Princess began to cry and said, 'I am a King's daughter, yet told to pick the lice off a fox! If only I were sitting at home in my bower, I should see the flowers in the garden!'

Then the fox knew that he had his true bride, and changed into the white manikin, who now became the Princess' husband. She had to live with him in a little hut and cook and sew for him for many a day; but, to be sure, the little man did all he could to please her.

One day the manikin said to her, 'I must go away, but soon three white doves will come flying by. They will fly quite close to the ground. Catch the one in the middle, and, when you've got it, cut off its head; but see to it that you take none other than the middle one or something dreadful will happen.' With that the little man went.

Before long the three white doves came flying by. The Princess eyed them closely, seized hold of the middle one, took a knife and cut off its head. Hardly had the head touched the ground when before her stood a handsome young Prince, who said, 'A fairy put me under a spell by which for seven years I had to lose my human form. I had then to fly past my wife as a dove between two others, and she had to catch me and cut my head off. If she failed to catch me, or took the wrong dove, once I was past it would be too late and never more could the spell be broken. That's why I asked you to be sure and take great care—for I am the manikin, and you are my wife.'

At this the Princess rejoiced, and together they went to her father. And when he died, they inherited his kingdom.

THE LION AND THE FROG

THERE once lived a King and a Queen, and they had a son and a daughter who loved each other dearly. The Prince was fond of hunting in the forest, but unhappily one day he did not return, and the Princess cried her eyes out for her dear brother. When she could bear it no longer, she set out in search of him. She tramped a long, long while through the forest, and, just when she was tired out and unable to go a yard further, she met a lion, who looked so kind that the Princess climbed on his back and rode away. Soon the lion was going at a quick trot, stroking the Princess with his tail the while; and after some time they arrived at a cave.

The lion at once padded inside; and though it was all dark within, the Princess was not afraid, as she did not realise that a lion could be wicked. The cave was very long, and at the far end they came out into the daylight again, where a big and beautiful garden appeared, surrounding a splendid palace. The lion stopped at the gates, and, when the Princess had slipped down from his back, he lost no time in telling her that from that time on she must live in his palace and work as his servant. But, if she worked well, she would one day find her brother again.

The Princess, cast down by her lot, walked about the garden, far from all her friends and lonely, with only the lion for company. But as she was walking to and fro, she suddenly noticed a pond with a small island in the middle, and on the island a tent in which squatted a very pretty green frog wearing a large rose-leaf as a bonnet.

'Why do you look so sad?' asked the frog; and, when the Princess told her story, the frog gently comforted her, saying, 'Come to me any time you want anything, and I'll help you all I can. Only I shall claim a reward from you every day—a fresh rose-leaf for a bonnet.' The Princess promised, and, whenever the lion demanded anything, she ran off to the pond and told the frog, who leapt away and got it.

One day the lion demanded a pie of midges, which the poor Princess had no idea how to obtain, but she went to her frog, who did not find the task hard at all. The frog quickly caught enough midges, gathered firewood, kneaded the dough and baked a most delicious pie. But, when the Princess reached out to take it, the frog said, 'You can only have it on one condition —that, the moment you see the lion is asleep, you cut off his head with the sword kept behind his couch.'

The Princess did not like to do this as the lion had been so good to her; but the frog warned her that, if she refused to do what was asked, she would never see her brother again. So the Princess plucked up courage and took the pie to the lion. It just suited him, and, when he had gobbled it all up, he felt very drowsy.

'Stroke me gently behind the ears,' he bade the Princess,

'until I fall asleep.' This the Princess did with her left hand, while with her right she reached behind the couch for the sword. 'What a shame to kill the poor lion!' she thought, but at last, closing her eyes and thinking of her dear brother, she struck a sharp blow.

Then what a fright she got to feel two arms clasped round her, and what joy when she heard a familiar voice, and opening her eyes in amazement saw, instead of a slain lion, her own brother. A wicked sorcerer had wanted her brother's sweetheart, and out of jealousy had turned him into a lion. Only a woman who for love of the Prince would kill the lion could break the spell.

Brother and sister now went into the garden to thank their friend, but were just in time to see the frog leap into a fire made of shavings. The fire burnt on until the frog was all consumed, and then out of the ashes stepped a lovely maiden in a leaf-green frock, with a wreath of roses on her head. The Prince saw that she was the fairy he had loved, who had changed herself into a frog to save him.

Soon the two became husband and wife; and then the Prince found another Prince to marry his good sister. From that time on, whenever the Princess rode on horseback, she spread the lion's skin over the saddle, and carried at her side the sword that had saved the life of her dear brother.

THE SIMPLETON

THERE was once a lad who was simple and, though he did whatever his mother told him, he always did it wrong.

At length he went to work. His master told him to go into the fields and sow, saying, 'Every year, fruit a hundredfold!' On the way the lad met some people carrying a dead body, and he said, 'Every year, a hundred!' Hearing this they gave him a hiding, and he went home and said to his mother, 'Oh Mother just think what's happened to me! Yet I only repeated what the master told me.' His mother replied, 'You ought to have said, "Rest in peace!"'

He set out afresh. Along came a knacker with a dead horse, and the lad said, 'Rest in peace!' The knacker resented his remark and he, too, gave him a hiding. So he went home and complained to his mother, who replied, 'You ought to have said, "Away with the carcass!"'

Once more he went into the fields, and a wedding party came along. 'Away with the carcass!' said he, and they, too, gave him a hiding. 'Oh Mother,' he said again, 'what a dreadful time I've had!' and told his tale. She replied, 'You ought to have said, "Here is joy and happiness!"'

He was on his way once again when he saw a house on fire and exclaimed, 'Here is joy and happiness!' Again the folk fell on him and gave him a hiding. Complaining to his mother he got the reply, 'You ought to have taken a bucket of water to help put the fire out.'

Next he passed some beehives, and, remembering the bucket of water, he poured one over the bees and killed them all. At that the beekeeper picked up a stick and drove him off.

'Oh Mother, what a dreadful time I've had!' She replied, 'You ought to have said, "Give me some too."' Then he happened to pass a byre where they were cleaning out the dung. The lad took off his cap and said, 'Give me some too.'

TWO CHILDREN IN A FAMINE

ONCE there was a mother who had two daughters and they were so poor that she hadn't the tiniest morsel of bread left to put in their mouths.

Now when their hunger grew unbearable the mother, driven distracted and in utter despair, said to her elder child, 'I'll have to kill you, for something to eat!' The girl answered, 'O dear Mother, spare me—I'll go out and see if I can get some food, without begging.' She went out and brought back a small piece of bread, and they shared it, but it wasn't big enough to satisfy their hunger.

Then the mother said to the other daughter, 'So it will have to be you.' But she answered, 'O dear Mother, spare me—I'll go out and get some food on the sly from somewhere.' She went out and came back with two small pieces, which they ate together, but it wasn't enough to satisfy their hunger.

A few hours later the mother spoke to them again. 'You must die after all. Otherwise all three of us will perish.' They answered 'Dear Mother, we'll lie down and sleep, and not get up till the Day of Judgment.'

So they lay down and fell into a deep sleep from which nobody could wake them.

But the mother vanished, and no one knows where she has got to.

OUR LADY OF SORROWS

ONCE upon a time there was a godly maiden who had vowed to the Lord never to marry. As she was most fair to look upon, her father opposed her vow and tried to force her into marriage. In her grief she prayed to the Lord to let her grow a beard; and this she at once did. Then the King, in his wrath, had her crucified, and she became a saint.

Now it chanced that a poor wandering fiddler came to the church where her statue was. He knelt down before it, and the saint was touched that he should be the first to have believed in her innocence; and, as the statue wore golden slippers, it loosen-ed one and let it drop for the benefit of the pilgrim. He bent down gratefully and picked up the gift.

But soon they missed the golden slipper in the church, and search was made for it everywhere, till at last it was found on the poor little fiddler. He was condemned as a wicked thief, and led through the town to be hanged. But, when the procession was passing the church where the statue stood, the fiddler asked if they would let him go in to bid a last farewell with his good fiddle, and tell the saint who had favoured him of the dire straits he was in. And they let him do so.

Hardly had he taken one step in the church when, lo and behold, the statue dropped the other golden slipper too, and thus proved that he was not a thief.

So they took off the fiddler's leg-irons and handcuffs, and he went on his way merrily. And they called the holy virgin Our Lady of Sorrows.

THE MANIKIN

ONE DAY I was going for a walk when I came to a thick wood, and there I met a Big Thing with a long, long tail —yards of it trailed behind!

Wanting a bit of fun, I seized hold of the long tuft of hair and let myself be dragged along, and in a little while we came to a big castle, and the Thing went in. I couldn't even tell where we were, as the Thing dashed through so many rooms and scraped me round the corners so that lots of cobwebs were brushed on to me.

All of a sudden I was stranded in a corner, and when I looked I saw there was still a big tuft of hair in my hand—I'd pulled it out of the Thing. So I laid the hair down and stayed put. Like a shot all the doors around me closed, and I'd no idea where the Thing had got to.

Suddenly a manikin stood before me and said, 'Good evening.' Said I, 'Good evening to you.' 'Why have you come here?'

Said I, 'Just for fun.' Then said the little man, 'Just see what you've done!—You've taken away our master's strength.' 'I! Well, when he simply wouldn't stop, I pulled out a bit of his tail.'

'Dear me, something dreadful's going to happen! There the Thing's lying, fighting for dear life, and he'll perish any moment!'

'A lot I care! All I want is to clear out of this place.'

Then the little man went on, 'I am King of sixteen dwarves. What will you give me if I make them guide you safely out of here? They've all had a good schooling and are wise in many things.'

Then I said, 'My mother has a cow and I have a goat: one of the two you shall have.'

So eight dwarves came with me. Reaching the front door, we saw a big dog, but the dwarves made a stick out of frogs' teeth, hit the dog with it, and it fell back. We went on our way for a while, till we came to a big lake. The dwarves coiled a rope of maidenhair and gossamer and with it they drew me across. On and on we trudged through the thick wood; and they knew exactly where the Thing had dragged me along before.

Following the same path they got me back to my mother's door. I told my mother where I had been, and she gave me the goat. I set the dwarves out in a row, the biggest taking the first place and the smallest coming last, like so many organ-pipes! Then I gave the goat a shove to make it run over to them—and my whole life long I haven't seen it again.

THE PRINCE WHO WAS BEWITCHED

MANY many years ago lived a woman who was very poor. Yet poor as she was, she longed for a child; but never did she have one. No day or night went by without her longing for one, more than a sick man yearns for fresh water or an innkeeper for merry guests.

Now it chanced that the woman's husband thought one day, 'I'll go to the wood and fetch sticks for the fire—that will get me out of the house, and I won't have to put up with her constant moaning!' Away he went, searched and chopped the whole day long, and came home in the evening with a stout bundle of wood which he threw down on the floor.

Then, lo and behold! the tiniest slippery snake stole out from under the brushwood. Hardly had the goodwife caught sight of him when she gave a deep sigh and said, 'Snakes have their little snakes, women have their babes, and in the whole world only I, poor wretch, am childless, like a tree that is cursed and bears no fruit!'

At these words the little snake raised his tiny head and looked at the woman, 'You wish for a child and haven't got one? Adopt me. I will love you as my true mother.'

At first the poor woman was sadly taken aback at hearing a snake talk. Soon, however, she picked up courage and answered, 'All right, I will, and if you are a good little snake, I'll take every care of you as if I had carried you under my heart.' Nor did the goodman mind if the baby snake stayed in the cottage and was brought up there.

The woman gave the snake a corner of the room to sleep in, and brought him milk and titbits every day. After a little while they were all used to each other—the goodfolk to the snake, and the snake to the goodfolk; in fact they couldn't call to mind a time when things had been otherwise.

But the little snake grew day after day, the more so for the good care taken of him, till, by the time he was fully grown, he was of giant size, almost too big for the room.

One day he looked up, saying, 'Father, I want to marry.'

'By all means,' answered the goodman. 'But what are we to

do about it? We'll look for a snake-girl to wed.'

'The snake and dragon tribe do not appeal to me—they creep about among thorns and bushes. No; I want the King's daughter. Run, little man; and don't keep me waiting too long, but go to the King and fetch her. If he asks you about the bride-groom, say he's a snake.'

So the goodman went in haste, not stopping to think too much about the matter; and, on arriving at the King's castle, he said, 'Your Majesty, do not blame the messenger for the message he bears! I am to convey to you the compliments of your daughter's bridegroom, and have come to fetch the bride.'

'Who, then, is he who wishes to wed my dove?'

'A snake, Your Majesty.'

These words made the King believe that the fellow was not in his right mind, and he thought of a way to get rid of him on the spot. 'Well spoken,' said he, 'but it's not all settled yet. My daughter will not accept the snake till he has turned all the apples, with the rest of the fruit in my pleasure-garden, into pure gold.'

The goodman returned and told this to the snake, who replied, 'Oh, is that all? Tomorrow morning, little man, go out at day-break into the street and pick up all the fruit pips and stones you can find, then take and sow them in the King's pleasance—and you will see!'

So hardly had the sun cast his first rays, when our goodman came out basket in hand and began picking up all the stones of peaches, cherries, apricots, and all kinds of plums lying among the rubbish and on the causeway. These he took and sowed in the King's garden.

Then before you could say 'Jack Robinson' the stones sprout-ed and put forth boughs, blossoms and fruit of red gold, so bright and shiny that the King was amazed. But, when he called to mind his promise, he was filled with dismay.

The snake cried, 'Little man, run and fetch the bride.' The

goodman went, thinking everything was all right now; but the King had never intended to let the snake really have his child. So he said, 'If the snake-bridegroom wants my dear daughter, he must first turn the wall and ground of my garden into precious stones. Otherwise he'll not get her.'

The goodman ran back and passed on the message. Then the snake said, 'Is that all? Tomorrow morning, when dawn lightens, gather all the potsherds you can find and put them down at the King's garden wall; and you'll be surprised!'

So, first thing the next morning, the man threw a sack over his shoulder and popped into it all the broken pots, bowls, pans, knobs, handles and other bits and pieces he could find and carried them, as he had been told, to the King's garden. In the twinkling of an eye, ground and wall glowed and glittered with the brightest diamonds, rubies, jaspers and emeralds—enough to blind anybody looking at them.

If the King had had a painful surprise the first time, he had a worse now; and he was quite downcast, as he had no idea what to say when the snake's messenger should come again to ask for his daughter.

Once more the snake cried, 'Little man, make haste, run and fetch home the bride.'

But by the time the goodman arrived, the King had already thought of a way out. 'I'm afraid we haven't got quite as far as that yet!' he said. 'If he wants my daughter, he must first turn the whole castle into pure gold.'

This message the goodman duly delivered. 'Is that all?' said the snake. 'It won't take long. Go and make a bundle of all manner of herbs—wild and garden—then touch the foundation of the King's castle with them, and you'll soon see what happens.'

The man went and fetched rue, chervil, fennel, rampion and nettle, tied them in a bundle, went to the castle walls and touched them with the herbs. In less time than it takes to tell, the castle began to shine and glitter with pure gold.

'Little man, run and fetch home the bride.'

Along went the goodman again, and, when the King caught sight of him in the distance, he already knew he had no further excuse or trick to put him off with. Calling to mind the treasures the snake had provided, and thinking it might not be so bad after all to have such a rich son-in-law, he said, 'Let the bride-groom come forth, and the wedding shall be held this very day.'

When the goodman had gone, the King called his daughter, who was very beautiful. Her name was Grauhilda. 'Dearest daughter,' he said, 'I have promised you to a strange suitor; but I must not break my word.'

'Dearest Lord and Father,' she answered, 'whatever you command, I shall be loyal and obedient.' And before she had finished speaking, a big sleek snake streaked towards them, at sight of which all the courtiers shook like reeds in the wind, the hearts of the King and Queen quaked with fear, and everyone fled in a panic. But Grauhilda remained, all alone, thinking, 'What has to be, will be anyway. My Father has chosen this consort for me, and no one should struggle against fate.' The snake rolled and twisted closer and closer till, almost up to Grauhilda, it swiftly coiled a number of loops with its tail so that she seemed to be sitting on a ring; then it bore her off to the wedding chamber.

Hardly were they alone in the room when the snake bolted the door, threw off his skin, and turned into the handsomest youth ever seen in the world. His locks shone on his head like the rays of the sun.

Now the old King had been stiff with fear to see his dearest child go off with the snake; indeed, if anyone had tried bleeding him at that moment, he would not have drawn a single drop of blood! Then on hearing the door being bolted, he was horrified beyond all bounds. 'Wife, can you hear?' he cried. 'The bolt has been shot and now that vile dragon has our darling child

entirely in his power. He will crush her as you would crush an egg in your hand.'

All the time he was itching to get near the room to listen and find if he could help her. He pressed close up to the door, and, as fortunately there was a chink, he was just able to peep inside—and saw the cast-off snake-skin lying on the floor and the handsomest youth you could imagine, resting in the bed next his daughter.

At this his heart thrilled with joy, and forcing the door, he picked up the snake-skin and threw it on the fire, where it shot up in flames. But when the bridegroom saw what had happened, he was beside himself, crying, 'Oh, what have you done to me!' Instantly he changed into a dove, flew up from the bed and tried to escape. But all the windows were closed. Then the dove frantically tapped with his small beak and head on one of the panes in order to force a way out. Unhappily the hole he made was not nearly large enough, and in frenzied haste he only got through at the cost of dreadful gashes from the broken edges of the glass.

So the poor young bride was left desolate as she saw her joy wrenched from her. Her father and mother comforted her all they could, but in vain. Then, as night fell, with the whole castle asleep, Grauhilda got up, took with her all the rings and jewels she possessed, and slipping through a secret little door made her way out of the royal castle, firmly resolved not to rest or tarry till she had found her beloved husband again.

The night was chill, and the moon shone down from the sky. A fox came brushing along, 'God be with you, fair maiden!'

'Thank you, Master Fox.'

'Will you let me come with you?'

'Well, why not! I am lost hereabouts.'

So, trudging along side by side, they came after a while to a dark forest where the trees whispered like children at play. By this time the wanderers were tired out with walking and sat down to rest among the bushes by a well of clear water. Then, making a cushion of green herbs, they laid their heads upon it and slept the whole night through.

At daybreak the next morning they woke up right merrily and got ready for the road. With the little forest birds twittering and warbling in the air high above the trees, it was a delight, and Grauhilda could hardly take a dozen steps without standing still and listening to the sweet bird-song that gave her such joy. The fox, noting this and giving himself a knowing air, said, 'You'd be even more delighted if you knew what the birds were saying!'

'Oh, if you understand their language, do tell me what they say.'

The girl was curious, as women are, but the fox was cunning, as foxes are, and let her go on begging, without telling her anything.

'Oh, do tell me, goodman fox!' said Grauhilda; 'then we'll walk together merrily all day long.'

As she never stopped asking, Master Fox in the end gave in and said, 'The birds tell of a dreadful disaster that has befallen a Prince. This youth was born as graceful as a slender tree; but a witch, falling in love with him and being spurned, took her revenge by changing him for the space of seven years into a snake. When the seven years were about up, he fell in love with a Princess, and married her. In the wedding chamber he stripped off the snake-skin and became a handsome youth. But the King, father of the bride, seeing the skin lying about, burnt it in the fire—and the youth couldn't remain any longer, but had to go. Taking the shape of a dove he tried to fly away, broke the window pane, and the glass gashed him so badly that no doctor would give a farthing for his life.'

You may well imagine how sad and at the same time joyful was Grauhilda to hear the story of her own misery—sad about her husband's suffering, but joyful to have news of him. Pretending innocence of all this, she asked, 'Who is this Prince and where does he live? It would indeed be grievous. if there were no cure for him.'

'There is a cure, only the doctors don't know it,' replied the fox. 'The birds said, "The Prince's father lives in a deep valley. Nothing on earth will cure the wounds in the Prince's head unless someone takes our blood—the blood of us birds who sing this—and rubs him with the ointment made from it." '

Then Grauhilda fell on her knees before the fox, 'Goodman and dear Master Fox, that would be a fine thing to do! Why shouldn't we cure the King's son and earn the reward? Go and catch me the little birds so that we can take their blood—for that service you shall be well looked after all your days.'

'Softly, softly,' answered the Fox. 'Wait till tonight when the little birds of many colours come flying home to roost on the big tree. There they will settle, on all the branches; and I'll climb up and catch them, one by one.'

They spent the whole day talking about the beauty of the bridegroom, the fright the old King had had, and the disaster brought on by his curiosity; and so the time slipped by, and at length night threw her mantle over the earth. Nor was it long before the birds came flying home one after another, crowding bough after bough and branch after branch. There they perched and closed their eyes.

Then Master Fox came slinking along softly, ever so softly, and climbed up the tree to seize the little birds, one after another, till he had caught a great many—little siskins and titmice on the first branch; hedge-sparrows and goldfinches on the second; on the third sparrows and linnets; on the fourth yellowhammers and nightingales; larks and swallows on the fifth; and right on the top wrens and flycatchers. The fox caught them, twisted their necks without mercy, and handed them down. Then Grauhilda took each little body and held it over a bottle to let the blood drip in without one drop being lost. In the end

Grauhilda jumped for joy to think they had done the job so well.

'Don't crow too soon, my daughter. You think you've done the trick, but truth to tell you've done nothing at all; for, if the birds' blood is to be of any use to you, it needs my good fox blood mixed with it! The bird's blood I can make use of myself.' And scarcely had the fox spoken these words when he laughed and took to his heels.

Grauhilda, though really alarmed, artfully flattered him with her woman's wiles, calling after him, 'Well, get away then, you foolish fox. You have good cause to flee!—as if I didn't owe you a great debt, and as if there were no more foxes in the world whose blood would serve me just the same! O poor maiden! never shall I find my way alone through the thick dark forest to the kingdom of Deep Valley, where the sick Prince is, unless you help me and show me all the highways and byways!' So the fox thought to himself, 'I can surely trust her;' and, believing nobody could be more cunning than himself, he was outwitted by a woman. He halted and waited for her. Then they went along together on the path through the dark forest.

Hardly had they gone fifty steps before Grauhilda raised the stick she was carrying and struck the fox on the head, so that he fell down full length—and lay there stone-dead. She bent down, carefully drained his blood and mixed it with that of the little birds. This done, she walked away as fast as she could, never stopping, and went on and on until she came to Deep Valley.

Arriving in the town she made her way directly to the castle and had herself announced as a doctor from a far land. The Prince's father was doubtful what a maiden could do when the greatest physicians had failed, but he thought that, if it didn't help, at least it could do no harm to let her try—though it seemed a waste of pains. So she was admitted.

First Grauhilda asked, 'What shall I get if I restore him to health?' Said the King, 'Whatever you ask.' He did not believe she could cure the Prince. Then she asked to have the youth as her husband; and the King agreed. Thus, having the King's word, she went into the sick-room and rubbed the Prince with the blood-ointment.

No sooner was this done than the patient sprang up as fit as a fiddle, as though nothing had ever been wrong with him. But Grauhilda, his dearest bride, he did not recognise, as she had disguised her face. She now came and asked for him in marriage, and the old King agreed that this was right and had been promised. To this the young man replied, 'No, no, for I've already given my promise to the most beautiful maiden in the world.'

So, seeing his faithfulness, Grauhilda went and washed her face, and he at once recognised her.

Then there was much merrymaking, the wedding was held again, and the pair ruled together in peace and happiness to the end of their days.

THE WILLOW WREN

ONE fine day in May the birds gathered together to choose their King who was to be the one that flew the highest. Came eagle and finch, owl and crow, lark and sparrow—in short they all came, including the cuckoo and the hoopoe; also a very tiny bird that hadn't any name! Then they all flew up from the fields in good time, early in the morning, that none might say afterwards, 'I could really have flown a little higher but evening was coming on and I didn't feel like it.' Now all had time enough to fly their very highest. And what a flustering and blustering there was on the ground!—it made the dust fly up; and what a buzzing up in the air!

The tiny bird soon fell behind, unable to climb farther. It was the eagle who flew the highest, so high indeed that he could have pecked out the sun's eyes. Seeing he was highest he thought, 'Why fly any higher? I'm King anyway!' Shortly after, he began to drop lower, and, far far below, the other birds clamoured 'You must be our King! No one has gone higher than you!' 'Except me!' piped the tiny bird without a name, who had hidden in the eagle's breast-feathers and was now rising high into the heavens, so high that he could see the Lord seated on His throne. At the very top of his flight he clapped his wings to and let himself drop till he touched the ground.

So the birds had to admit that the tiny one had flown the highest of all. But, as he had done so only by guile and cunning, they did not want him as their King. On the contrary they wanted him arrested and dealt with by the law for trickery and cheating.

The tiny bird's little heart trembled at this and in his terror he slipped into a mousehole. Then the rest of the birds set the owl on guard before the hole, telling him on no account to let the villain escape, if he valued his life! So there stood the owl all day long watching the hole, and he didn't close an eye. At nightfall the other birds, tired out with so much flying, went to roost, wives, children and all. Only the owl stayed awake.

But he, too, was tired, and said to himself, 'One eye I might close, keeping good watch with the other, and the little rascal won't be able to escape from the hole.' So the owl shut one eye and fixed the other firmly on the mousehole. The little bird popped his head out and was just going to slink off when the owl, in a flash, swooped in front—and back went his head! Once more the owl kept one eye open and closed the other; and so he meant to go on all night.

But next time the owl closed one eye, he failed to open the other; and the little bird, peeping out of his hole, saw his guard asleep, and off he flew. So, when the birds expected to hold the trial next day, the wicked rascal was gone!

From that time on the owl has never dared be seen by day, or the other birds would chase and set upon him for letting the little bird escape. He only goes about at night, when the rest of the birds are asleep. The tiny bird, too, is shy of being seen, as he is always scared lest they catch him. He skulks about gardens and hedges, and the birds out of spite call him 'King of the Hedges'!

THE ROBBER AND HIS SONS

THERE was once a robber whose haunt was a dense forest, where he lurked in ravines and rocky caves with his band. When princes and lords or rich merchants travelled the highway, he lay in wait and robbed them.

But as he grew older this way of life satisfied him no more, and he repented his ill deeds. He took to better things, working honestly and doing good to others whenever he could. People were astonished at the sudden change, and pleased about it.

Now the robber had three sons, and when they were grown up he called them before him and said, 'Dear sons, tell me what trade you wish to learn to make an honest living.'

Having talked the matter over among themselves, they replied, 'We are chips of the old block, and wish to live the way you have lived: we want to be robbers. A trade where you have to slave and slave, morning, noon and night, with little gain and a hard struggle, is not for us.'

'Oh, my dear boys,' answered the father, 'why won't you live quietly and be content with little? Honesty is the best policy, after all. A robber's life is wicked and ungodly, and leads to a bad end. You won't enjoy the wealth you plunder. I know how I have felt with it all. I warn you, you will come to no good. The pitcher goes to the well till one day it breaks. You'll be caught in the end, and hanged on the gallows.' But the sons would not heed his words: they stood by what they'd said.

It was their wish to show their mettle right away. They knew that the Queen had a fine horse in her stable, worth a lot of money; and this they proposed to steal. They knew, too, that the horse would eat nothing but the juicy grass that grew in a certain damp wood. So they went there, cut some grass, and made a big bundle of it. The two older lads stuffed the youngest and smallest inside it, so that he couldn't be seen, and took the bundle to market.

The Queen's Master of the Horse bought it, and had it carried to the stable and put down on the floor. When midnight struck and all the palace was asleep, the little lad crept out of the bundle, loosed the horse, and put on it the golden bridle and the gold-embroidered horse-cloth—but its little bells he stuffed with wax, so as to make no noise. Then he unlocked the stable door and rode off at top speed to the place his brothers had appointed.

But the city guards caught sight of the robber and gave chase. Overtaking him outside the town with his brothers, they arrested all three and put them in prison. Next morning they were led into the Queen's presence. Seeing they were three well-set-up lads, she asked where they came from, and was told they were the sons of the old robber who had changed his ways and become an obedient subject.

She ordered them back to prison, and had the father asked if he was prepared to ransom them. The old man came and said, 'My sons are not worth one penny's ransom.'

Then the Queen addressed him, 'You are well-known as a one-time evildoer. Tell me the strangest adventure in your life as a robber, and I'll give you back your sons.'

On hearing this the old man began, 'Hearken to my words, Your Majesty, and I'll tell you the story of what frightened me more than flood or fire.

'I heard that in a wild and wooded cleft between two mountains, full twenty miles from any human soul, dwelt a giant, guarding a rich treasure of many thousand gold and silver coins. So I picked about a hundred of my band and off we went, following a long and toilsome path between great boulders and precipices. We were relieved to find the giant was away, and took as much of the gold and silver as we could carry. We were just on the point of going, thinking ourselves quite safe, when without warning the giant and nine of his fellows set on us and took us all prisoners. They then shared us out equally, each giant getting ten.

'With nine others I fell to the lot of the giant whose treasure we had plundered. After tying our hands behind our backs, he drove us like sheep into his rocky cave. We offered to pay a ransom in goods and money, but he answered, "What use is your treasure to me? I'll keep you and eat your flesh—that suits me far better!"

'He felt over each of us, and choosing one he said, "He's the plumpest. I'll start with him." He felled the man, flung his cut-up flesh into a pan of water, set it on the fire, and, when the meat was cooked, ate his dinner. So every day he ate another of us, and, as I was the leanest, I was to come last.

'Now, when my nine comrades had been eaten and I saw my turn coming, I thought of a trick. "I notice you have bad eyes," I said to the giant, "and your sight is suffering. I am a doctor, and highly skilled in my art: I will heal your eyes if you will but spare my life." He promised to do so, if I could cure him; and gave me everything I asked for the treatment. I poured oil into a pan, mixed sulphur, pitch, salt, arsenic and other vile things into it, then set the pan on the fire, as if making a plaster for his eyes. When the oil began to simmer I bade the giant lie down; and I poured the whole pan over his eyes, neck and belly, so that he lost his sight completely, and the skin burned and shrivelled up all over his body.

'With a hideous roar he jumped up, then threw himself on the ground, rolling and squirming about, and screaming and bellowing with the pain like a lion or a bull. In a rage he got on to his feet, seized a huge club, and rushing round the house he beat on the floor and against the wall in the hope of hitting me. Escape I could not, for everywhere the house was shut in by high walls and the gates were locked with iron bars. I dodged about from one corner to another, till at last I could do nothing but get up a ladder to the roof and cling with both my hands to the rafters.

'There I hung for a day and a night, but when I couldn't stand it any longer I climbed down and got amongst the sheep. I had to be pretty spry, always running in between the giant's legs with the animals so as not to be picked out. At length I found the skin of a ram lying in a corner among the sheep; so I slipped into it, carefully arranging for the animal's horns to stand right on my head. It was the giant's custom to make the sheep run between his legs before going out to pasture, while he counted them and grabbed the fattest. This he cooked for his dinner. In an attempt to escape I squeezed between his legs like the other sheep, but when he felt me and found I was heavy he cried, "You're fat—you shall fill my belly today." With a spring I slipped out of his grasp, but he got me again. I escaped once more, but he got me back; and so it went on seven times—till he was so maddened that he roared, "Get out! And may the wolves devour you! You've fooled me to your heart's content!"

'Once outside I cast off the skin, shouted mockingly that I'd got away after all, and chaffed him without mercy. Pulling a ring off his finger he retorted, "Take this gold ring as a gift— you well deserve it. It's not right that such a smart, cunning chap should leave me without a present."

'I took the ring and slipped it on my finger, little dreaming it carried a spell with it. But from the instant it was on my finger I had to keep on shouting the whole time, "Here I am, here I am!" whether I liked it or not. Always knowing now where I was, the giant followed me into the wood; but, in his blindness, he ran every few moments against a branch or a tree-trunk and fell down like a mighty tree himself. But he promptly got up again, and, with his long legs and big strides, he always caught me up and almost touched me as I kept on shouting, "Here I am, here I am!" Of course I realised that the ring was the cause of my outcries and I struggled to pull it off; but I simply couldn't. There was only one thing for me to do—bite the finger off with my own teeth! From that moment I ceased my clamour, and was lucky enough to get away from the giant. I had lost my finger, I must admit, but my life was saved.

'Your Majesty,' the robber went on, 'I've told you this tale to get one of my sons freed; now, to free the second one, I'll tell you what happened next.

'Having escaped from the hands of the giant, I roamed about in the wilderness, not knowing which way to turn. I climbed the highest pines and clambered to the mountain peaks, but, wherever I gazed, far and wide, there wasn't a house or a field or any sign of human life, nothing anywhere, in fact, but fearful wilderness. From the crests almost touching the sky I went down into the valleys, but they were a mass of sheer rock-faces. I met lions, bears, buffaloes, wild donkeys, and poisonous snakes, horrible serpents and other reptiles. I saw savage hairy men with horns and beaks, so hideous that I still shudder to think of them. I pressed on and on. Hunger and thirst tormented me, and every moment I feared I should sink down with fatigue.

'At long last, just as the sun was setting, I came to a high mountain, whence, in a deserted valley, I beheld smoke rising from an oven newly fired. I ran helter-skelter down the mountain slope towards the smoke, only, when I got there, to see three dead men hanging from the branch of a tree. Panic seized me as I pictured myself falling into the hands of another giant; and I was in dread of my life. But I took courage, went on and found a cottage.

'The door stood wide open, and beside the fire on the hearth sat a woman with her child. I entered, wished her the time of day, and asked why she was sitting there so lonely and where her husband was. I also asked if it was far to the nearest house. She answered that the land of men was far far away; and with tears in her eyes she told how, the night before, the wild monsters from the wood had come and kidnapped herself and the child from her husband's side and brought them to this wilderness. That morning the monsters had gone away, after ordering her to slay the child and cook him, as they intended eating him on coming home.

'When I had heard the story, my heart melted for the woman and child, and I resolved to rid them of their terror. I hurried to the tree where the three thieves had been hanged, cut down the middle one, who was stout, and carried the body to the cottage. I cut him into pieces and told the woman to give these to the giant for his dinner; but the child I took and hid in a hollow tree. As for myself I kept out of sight behind the house, where I could watch for the wild men's approach and, if need arose, rush to the woman's rescue.

'Just before sunset I caught sight of the monsters, who came running down the mountain—hideous and horrible they were to behold, like apes. They were dragging a dead body behind them, but I could not make out whose it was. Once in the cottage, they lit a blazing fire, tore the bleeding body asunder with their teeth, and devoured it. Next they took off the fire the pan the thief's flesh had been boiled in, and divided the pieces among themselves for their dinner.

'After the meal the one who appeared to be their leader asked the woman if what they had eaten had been the flesh of her child. The woman replied, "Yes." But the monster said, "I believe you have hidden your child and cooked us one of the thieves that hang on the tree!" Then he sent three of his band to run out and bring him a slice of flesh from each of the three thieves, as proof that they were still there.

'On hearing this, I dashed ahead of them and with my two hands hung myself up on the rope between the two thieves, in the place from which I had removed the third body. Now, when the monsters came, they cut a slice off each body's loins. They took a piece out of mine as well, but I bore it without making so much as a murmur. In proof I still have the scar on my body.'

Here the robber was silent for a moment; then he went on, 'This story, Your Majesty, I have told you on behalf of my second son. For my third I shall relate the end of the adventure.

'When the wild men had hurried off with the three pieces of flesh, I let myself down again and dressed my wound as best I could with strips torn off my shirt. The blood wouldn't stop flowing, and simply streamed down. However, I paid no further attention to it. My only thought was how to keep my promise to the woman, and save both her and the child. So I ran back to the cottage, kept hidden, and listened to what was going on. But it took me all my time to hold out, for the wound was painful and I was weak with hunger and thirst.

'The leader duly tasted the three slices of flesh that had been brought to him, and after trying the one cut from me, and still bleeding, he said, "Run and fetch me the thief in the middle; his flesh is still fresh and I like it!" On hearing this I hastened back to the gallows and hung myself again on the rope between the two dead men. In a trice the monsters arrived, took me off the gallows, and dragged me over thorns and thistles to the cottage, where they laid me down on the floor. They sharpened their teeth and their knives over me, and got ready to kill and eat me.

'They were all set to lay hands on me when such a storm broke out, with lightning, thunder and a gale of wind, that they took fright themselves, and fled with terrible bellows, out of windows, doors and even the roof, leaving me on the floor.

117

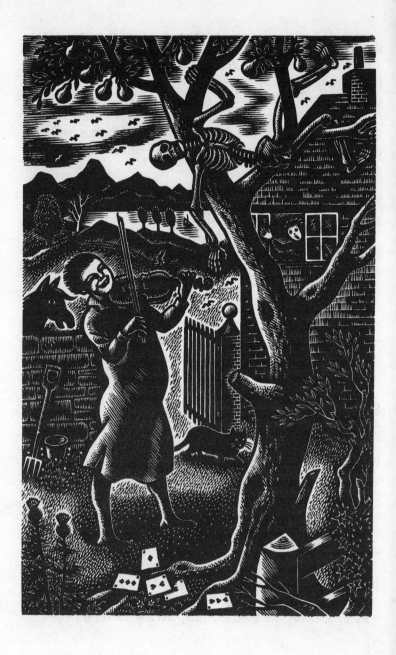

'Three hours later, as dawn came and a bright sun rose, I set off walking, the woman and her child with me. For forty days we tramped the wilderness, eating nothing but roots, berries and herbs growing by the wayside. At last I came to where men dwelt. The woman and child I took back to the husband; and you can well imagine his joy!'

With that the robber ended his story.

'By saving the woman and her child you have atoned for much of your evil-doing,' said the Queen. 'I will let your three sons go.'

JOLLY HANS

JOLLY HANS had fallen on evil days: once a rich man, he had lost everything at cards. Then it happened that our Lord and St. Peter came down to the earth and appeared at his door. They knocked and said, 'Good evening, Jolly Hans, can you put us up for the night?'

'Why not?' answered Jolly Hans, 'if you'll take us as we are. The goodwife and I have nothing but a bundle of straw, but, if you will be content with that, you are welcome, to be sure.'

'Why not?' said our Lord and St. Peter.

So they sat down and talked of old times, and St. Peter said, 'We're both thirsty, Jolly Hans. Do fetch us a jug of beer; here's the money.'

That suited our Hans down to the ground. He went to the inn, heard them playing cards, joined in, and the money was gone in no time.

'What shall I do?' thought he; 'where shall I now get beer for those folk sitting at home thirsty?'

However, he went back and said he'd fallen and broken the jug with the beer. To this St. Peter replied, 'For once I'll give you the money again; but see you bring the jug safely back this time, we are dry as a bone.'

'How can I,' thought he, 'if they are still playing cards?'

But he went off with the jug, plugged his ears so that he couldn't hear them playing, and got back happily with the beer.

When our Lord and St. Peter had drunk their fill they began to feel hungry. 'What shall I do?' thought the goodwife. 'I've no flour, I'll just have to make a pancake of the ashes.'

So they sat down together and ate, while Jolly Hans chattered about playing cards and how merry that was. They talked and talked till at last their eyes began to droop. Our Lord and St. Peter lay down on the straw, and Jolly Hans and his wife by the fire.

When they got up in the morning and our Lord and St. Peter were about to leave, they gave Jolly Hans three things: a pack of cards that when dealt would make him win every game, dice that when thrown would always make him the winner, and a fiddle which, when he began to play it, would make everything stick where it was.

Jolly Hans now began merrily playing at cards again, and he always won. Once more he bought himself a fine house, and his cards and fiddle he took with him wherever he went.

At last Jolly Hans fell ill, and Death came and said, 'Jolly Hans, you must die.' 'Oh, good old Death,' he said, 'just pick me a pear from the tree before the house!' Then, when Death was safely up the tree, Jolly Hans began playing his fiddle, and Death found himself stuck on the tree.

So again Hans began playing cards and dice, until one day a cousin died and he had to go to the funeral. When the man was buried, Jolly Hans earnestly repeated the Lord's Prayer. . . . 'Ah,' cried Death, 'that's what I've waited for—to catch you praying! Now you must come away!'

So Jolly Hans died, and knocked at the gates of Heaven. 'Who's there?'

'Jolly Hans.'

'It's Hell that you must go to.'

When Hans came to Hell he knocked.

'Who's there?'

'Jolly Hans.'

'What do you want here?'

'To play cards.'

'What will you play for?'

'Souls.'

So Jolly Hans played, and won a hundred souls; and he took them on his back and knocked at the gates of Heaven.

'Who's there?'

'Jolly Hans, with a hundred souls, not one less——'

'No!—go away again.'

So he went back to Hell and knocked.

'Who's there?'

'Jolly Hans. We'll play for souls again!'

And after winning another hundred souls, he went back to Heaven and knocked.

'Who's there?'

'Jolly Hans with two hundred souls, not one more or less. Just let me peep into Heaven once.'

So St. Peter opened the gates, and Jolly Hans flung his pack of cards inside. 'Oh, let me get my cards back,' he shouted. Then he sat himself on his pack of cards, and there he remains to this very day.

THE SHROUD

A GRAVE-DIGGER once dug a grave for the child of a rich nobleman. He saw at the burial that she was wearing a little shroud of the finest linen, and thought to himself, 'A great pity for that to go under the ground! When the funeral is over I'll take it off her.'

The same night he opened the grave. But, when he saw the tender child lying there so innocent, he couldn't bring himself to take off the little shroud, but was contented with cutting out the tiny sleeves; then he closed the grave again.

The next night, however, the child came to his door in the moonlight, shivering with cold, and said, 'Give me my sleeves back! Give me my sleeves back!' But the grave-digger turned to the wall as if he hadn't seen anything, and buried his ears deep in the pillows.

The following night the child came again, 'Give me my sleeves back! Give me my sleeves back!' Again he turned away.

Now when all was quiet, the goodwife said, 'Why, haven't you dug the child's grave deep enough? Or have you put something in the coffin, that the little thing can't stay in her grave?' She asked and asked till at last he told her. Then she urged him, if the child came again, to give her back the sleeves.

The third night she came right to the middle of the room. 'Give me my sleeves back! Give me my sleeves back!'

Then the grave-digger threw her the sleeves, and the child vanished.

ILL LUCK

WHEN ill luck calls, though you may creep round corners or flee into the open fields, it will find you out all the same.

There was once a man who was so poor that he hadn't even a stick to keep the fire going on his hearth. So he went into the wood to cut down one of the trees; but they were all too big and sturdy. Deeper and deeper he pressed into the wood till at last he found one he could cope with.

Just as he was lifting his axe, he became aware of a pack of wolves breaking from a thicket and panting and howling towards him. He flung down his axe, took to his heels and came to a bridge. But the deep waters had worn away the supports, and the instant he made to step on it, it crashed and shattered to bits.

What was he to do? If he stood and waited for the wolves they would rend him in pieces. In his great need he risked jumping into the water, and, as he couldn't swim, he at once sank.

Some fishermen, sitting on the farther shore and seeing the man splash into the water, swam out and brought him safely to the bank. They stood him up against an old wall to get warmed in the sun and recover his strength. But, when he came out of his faint and tried to thank the fishermen and explain what had happened, the old wall collapsed and buried him beneath it.

THE DEAD MAN AND
THE PRINCESS
FREED FROM SLAVERY

ONCE upon a time there were three brothers who set out in three ships to sail the high seas. When they came to land, the youngest went to an inn, and when he saw in the kitchen a poor man stuck fast in the chimney he said to the innkeeper, 'Why is that man stuck there? I'll let him out.' 'No,' replied the innkeeper, 'he shan't be let out till he's paid his bill.' Then the youngest brother stayed on for three days and sold all he had, but by that time the poor fellow in the chimney was dead; so he paid for him to be given Christian burial.

When he went down to the sea-shore he found that his brothers had sailed. He followed their ships in a barge, but when he fell in with them again, they sold him as a slave to the Sultan of Turkey. Now this Sultan had a daughter and she took a great fancy to the slave, for he was good-looking and could sing and play the flute.

Then the Sultan chanced to capture another ship, and in it a girl of noble birth with her five maids. The girl was forced to do drudgery, and the slave's duty was to harness her and her maids to a plough and make them turn up the soil. The Sultan's daughter, watching him, went to her father, kissed his hands and feet, and then said, 'Dear Father, I beg you to give me the slave in marriage.' The Sultan flared up and answered, 'You, my wealthy daughter, want this poor sailor fellow for husband!' 'Well, then, let it be!' she answered. 'But if I can't have the sailor I must die in my bloom.'

So the father gave his consent. The slave now asked his promised wife to plead for the six slave-girls too, as he could not bear any longer to see them toiling and moiling at the plough. 'Well,' answered the father, 'since you are my only daughter, I'll grant you that as well. But now get into your carriage with your groom, and show him the whole land.'

So it was done. There were many carriages: in one sat the bride and her groom, in another the noble young lady, in yet another the maids, and in others the wedding guests. There were still more with bandsmen playing on horns and trumpets the finest music you could think of. They drove through the length and breadth of the country, and, when they came down to the sea, the bridegroom said, 'Now that we have seen the whole land, my bride must see what it's like on the water. Come, my dearest; but first allow me to speak to the six maidens, and then I'll come back to you.'

But after seeing the six maidens on to a boat he came back to the carriage of the Sultan's daughter and said, 'You're a sweet girl—but I've got myself betrothed to the stranger lady: do you wish to bid a sad farewell and go back to your father, or will you come with us to our own country?'

The Sultan's daughter wept bitterly; but returned with the

wedding guests to her father, while the sailor lad with his bride and her five maids went back to his homeland.

Once ashore he settled in a small house and earned an honest living, while the five maids sewed and knitted. When half a year had gone, there arrived a fine baby boy. 'Oh! if only my father, the King of England, could see him, he would be over⸗joyed!' said his wife.

Her husband clasped his hands with astonishment to hear that she was the King of England's daughter. And, after another two months had passed, his pretty wife came down one morning saying, 'My dear John, I dreamt last night that you went to see my father, and he received you with open arms. Would you like to cross the water and see him?' 'O yes,' he answered, 'I should dearly like to.'

Then his spouse went to her chest and got out three red flags finely embroidered, saying to him, 'My dear husband, as your ship nears England fly these three flags in the wind.' So when he approached the coast he did so; but the English sailors, seeing the three flags, boarded the ship and captured it, for none but the King's own ship might fly such princely flags.

They cast him into prison, where he was kept so many months that he grew a long beard; but at last the judge gave sentence that in three days he should die. The condemned man then sent the King a little cloth his wife had given him, for on it she had embroidered a message in letters of gold. When the King read this, he sent an order to the prison for the man to be brought before him. He would not go until his beard was shaved off; but at length he appeared before the King, and then gave him other cloths and told his story.

With all his heart the King rejoiced, and said, 'So my child Theresa lives, and I can be happy once more! My dear John, your dear wife, my daughter, shall be brought back to England to the sound of music.' Then all the King's friends and kinsmen assembled, and set out by ship with John and the musicians to fetch the Princess. But, on the return voyage with the mother and her child, there was a wicked servant on board. He wanted to marry the Princess himself and pushed John overboard, telling the Princess he would do the same to her if she said a word about it. But John, clinging on to three floating planks, managed to struggle near the shore, and at last, as a voice called to him urging, 'Keep on, John, keep on!' he reached firm ground. Then he saw before him the man he had found stuck in the chimney long ago, who now said to him, 'Wish for something.'

'I wish to be in England.'

'You'll be there instantly, and find your wife. She is having a church built, where she will be forced to marry the wicked servant. You must ask to work at the church yourself for twelve days.'

At once he found himself in England, and going up to the master builder he asked for twelve days' work. While he was busy working away, the Princess appeared with six black horses; and when John saw her he wiped himself with a black cloth she herself had given him. . . .

[Here the story breaks off, without telling of the happy reunion.]

DEAD MAN'S THANKS

ONCE there was a tailor's boy who was fond of travel, but all he had was three silver pieces. As he was passing the gallows outside the town, he saw a poor sinner hung up, and said to him, 'I'm sorry to see you hanging there for everybody to make game of.' So he went to the judge and asked to have the poor sinner's body. The judge replied, 'No, you can't have that, he deserved all he got.' But the tailor persisted, 'Please do give him to me, and you shall have my three silver pieces.'

The judge giving in at last, the lad went and cut the man

down from the gallows, buried him and said, 'Rest there in the name of the Lord!' This done, he moved on and came to a thick wood, where he met an uncannily tall fellow who looked so fearsome that the lad was terrified. The fellow said to him, 'Where are you going?'

'I want to see the world, I'm a tailor.'

'Well,' replied the weird fellow, 'I'll be your servant.'

Oh dear,' said the tailor alarmed, 'I've nothing to live on myself!'

'Never mind, come along,' said the fellow.

So along they went to the town and into a tailor's where the tall fellow bought three suits embroidered with silver and gold. Then they passed on to the Emperor's Court, and the tall fellow gave out that a young knight had arrived in the town, who would like to join in the mid-day meal. When they asked the name, he said, 'He is my master; but his name I may not tell. It's a secret.'

The young man appeared at mid-day, and was well received; indeed, as he was very handsome and polite, everybody wished to sit beside him. Meanwhile the tall fellow stood behind his chair and waited on him.

After the meal they played cards, and the lad won everything, nearly twelve thousand crowns. They asked him back for supper too, but, as the tall fellow told him he must now leave, he thanked everyone and left.

The tall fellow then hired him a carriage and six horses, he got into it, and they drove off to the wood. There, when they saw a fine old castle, the tall fellow knocked at the gate and shouted, 'Hail, old man! Open to us: my master's to live here.'

Out came a grey-haired old man with a beard that swept down to his shoes, and a coat thrown over his shoulders, who exclaimed, 'Oh, leave me in peace! I have seven brothers in chains down in a dungeon, and, if once they got loose, they'd knock the whole place down. No one can live here.'

'All right,' said the tall fellow; 'but my master shall!'

'I'll gladly give you anything you ask, but do leave me in peace!' said the grey-haired man.

'Then give my master a gold carriage, with six black horses, a gold sword, a gold watch and a million silver pieces!'

And the old man gave him everything.

But when the tailor had received all these, the castle sank into the ground—and he couldn't even trace where it had stood.

Then the tall fellow asked him if he knew who was beside him.

'No,' said the tailor.

'I am the poor sinner you took from the gallows. There are ghosts of seven kinds. I belong to the grateful ones.'

And he vanished.

But the tailor had plenty to live on for the rest of his days.

THE FAITHFUL WIFE

THERE was once a Count who had not been married a year before he had to go on a journey; and he fell into slavery in Turkey. Though he lived just like the other slaves, his shirt was never soiled. This was told to the Turkish King, who ordered him to present himself and explain how this was.

He said that he was a Count and had a very beautiful wife. She had given him the shirt, which would not soil unless he was unfaithful to her. Then the King bade him write to his wife and command her to come, and he would be set free. The Count was alarmed to hear this, and secretly sent his wife word to go into hiding, as the Turkish King had given orders to have her brought to him.

Some days later the King sent one of his servants to fetch the lady, but, when he arrived at the Count's castle, she was gone. Furious at this the man began storming and raving like a madman; but it helped him no whit, as he could not find her anywhere.

The Countess had her hair cut off and dressed herself as a pilgrim, carrying her harp which she could play most sweetly. Not a soul would recognise her in that disguise. She went down to the ship the furious Turk was on and spoke to the captain. 'I am a poor pilgrim and have a great desire to visit the land of the Turks. Do take me with you.' The captain answered, 'No, it can't be done, as I have a Turk on my ship who lays about him like a fiend at not finding the lovely Countess.' Then the pilgrim said, 'I could manage all right if you allowed me just to lie under the companion-way.' The captain at length agreed and she lay down under the stairway and played on her harp. When the Turk heard the music, it pleased him so much that he took the pilgrim before the King to play.

One day the pilgrim walked with the King in the garden where the poor slaves were working, the Count among them. Then the pilgrim began playing on the harp and sang:

'Of late in a garden myself I did find
With the fairest of flowers of many a kind:
Of these above all 'twas a rose I did prize
And hoped that her heart would respond to my eyes.

O noblest of flowers, full armed with sharp thorn,
By thee this frail body is cruelly torn;
But for thy dear sake those wounds I can bear
So long as I know that for me thou dost care.

Most sadly this garden have I now left—
Not a soul will demand what my heart hath bereft!
But too well do I know it—yet may nothing declare,
Since Heaven means to plague my heart with despair.

O woe worth the day!—the wrong course have I ta'en,
And what dearly I seek I ne'er can obtain!—
No longer, O rose, 'tis for me thou wert grown,
For another may pluck thee and call thee his own!'

Thus did she sing; and, when the Count heard the song, he thought he knew the voice, though the pilgrim did not make herself known.

The King so took to her that she had to be always about and play on her harp. She agreed to remain with the King on condition that three Christian slaves were set free. When the King promised, the pilgrim picked them out, the Count and two others.

Now, when the ship was ready to leave with the three on board, the pilgrim asked the captain to sail past her window. Then she swung from the window on to the ship and got away safely. As they were sitting together on board, the Count said, 'In the Turkish land there was such a lovely girl—I liked her so much that I'm disappointed I could not say good-bye to her.' But the moment the words were out, his shirt was soiled, and his wife in the pilgrim's habit was sorely troubled at her husband's unfaithfulness. Yet she still held back and did not reveal herself.

They arrived safe and sound in Germany; but, as they went on shore, the Countess asked the captain to hold the Count back awhile before letting him leave for his castle. Meantime she ran ahead and put on her own clothes, with a wig of most lovely hair. Then she went to meet her husband, who was overjoyed to see his wife again. They sat down at table, and the Count, after telling the story of the good pilgrim, said he couldn't understand why he was so long in coming. Then the lady got up, put on her pilgrim's habit and taking up her harp went back to her husband in the room. She then sang the song she had sung in the garden in the Turkish land.

The Count now recognised the pilgrim as his wife and realised it was she who had rescued him from slavery. Kneeling at her feet he begged forgiveness for having almost betrayed her. But his good wife drew him up and kissed him, saying that all was forgiven and forgotten. They sat down at table again, ate and drank, and lived happily to the end of their days.

But the harp and the pilgrim's habit they hung in the chapel of the castle, so that they should always remember.

THE SENTRY AND THE PRINCESS IN THE COFFIN

ONCE upon a time lived a King and a Queen, and they had no children. One day the King was so sore at heart that he exclaimed, 'Oh! that I had a child—though he were the Devil himself!' Soon afterwards the Queen gave birth to a daughter; but as she was as black as a raven—and as ugly—people were quite terrified at the sight of her. She roared like a beast, and was strange in every way.

When she was twelve years old she asked the King to have a grave dug for her, and, as he refused, she began howling so horribly that he gave way in sheer terror and had a grave made behind the altar in the church. She lay down in the grave, and they put over it a lid that she could lift. By her order six soldiers guarded the grave at night; but, when people entered the church next morning, they found that the Princess had killed them. The second night six more soldiers kept vigil by the grave, and she killed those too. So it went on for two whole years.

One day, while out walking, the King met a lad and said to him, 'Where are you going, my son?' The lad answered, 'I seek to get apprenticed to a cobbler or a tailor.' 'What's your name?' asked the King. 'My name's Frederick.' Then the King said,

'I don't want you to do that—come and be a soldier of mine. You shall be an officer or whatever you like, only you must stand guard by my daughter's grave for one night.' But Frederick did not like the idea at all, as he well knew what happened to the guards. The King pressed him so hard, however, that at length he gave way.

In the evening, when he went into the church, he lost courage and ran away. Outside the town gate he met a white manikin, who said to him, 'Where are you going, my son?' Frederick replied, 'I'm just taking a little walk.' But the manikin answered, 'I know well enough you are going to desert, because you're afraid the Princess will kill you. But go back: she won't harm you. And now I'll tell you what you must do. When you go into the church, you must stretch out both your arms, kneel down before the altar, and all the while pray, thinking of Our Lord. On no account must you leave the spot.'

Frederick did just as the white manikin had bidden. Then, as the clock struck eleven, the Princess rose from her grave, picked up a sword, and slashed Frederick with it until blood streamed from him. But he felt no pain, and kept on praying to the Lord. The Princess then started to howl so dreadfully that even the good folk in the town could hear her. Next she bade him leave the church. But he did not even rise, and the Princess went on slashing him till twelve struck. Then she went back into her grave.

Now when the King came to the church next morning to see how Frederick had fared, he found him still kneeling before the altar, praying. The King was astounded, and all the towns-folk rejoiced.

The same night six soldiers again stood guard, and again she killed them all. The third night Frederick was to watch once more. But when he got inside the church he took panic and ran away. Outside the gate, he again met the white manikin, who told him not to be afraid, but this night he should lie flat on his face at full length before the altar, on no account look up, and keep on praying all the time.

So Frederick went back and did everything the white manikin had bidden him. When the clock struck eleven, the black Princess appeared, started howling horribly and slashed at him. But he kept on praying to the Lord, till it was midnight and she went back to her grave.

On finding Frederick still alive the King was dumbfounded at the miracle of it and promised him a rich reward of gold and silver if he would watch by the Princess for one more night. This Frederick was by no means anxious to do, for he thought, 'Tonight she is sure to kill me—I'd rather run as far as my legs will carry me!'

He stole off again, but when he got outside the gate the white manikin came up to him and said, 'My son, tonight you must watch by the grave again, and this time you'll get your reward. When the Princess rises, at once lie down in her grave yourself, praying all the time and thinking constantly of the Lord. And however much she bids you get out of her grave, you must not do so until she stands before you all snow-white. Then, when she begins to cry, you may rise.'

Now when Frederick got to the church, he prayed fervently to the Lord; and when eleven struck, the Princess got up, and he at once lay down in her grave. At this she started screaming abuse at him and howling so hideously that you might have thought the whole church was tumbling down. But all the time Frederick kept praying to the Lord.

At last she began begging and pleading with him to get out of her grave, promising that, if he did, she would not harm him. He glanced up and noticed that she had a little white spot over her eyes; and, when next he looked, her forehead was all white; and then her whole face. He prayed earnestly to the Lord, and just before midnight she stood before him all snow-white and radiant as the sun.

Now she began weeping, and said, 'Get up, I beg you, dear Frederick. I won't harm you any more, for you have broken the spell.' And, while she was saying this, the clock struck twelve, and he got up.

Then she said that for fourteen years she had been under a spell, as her father had declared he must have a child even if it were the Devil himself. As she spoke, all the graves opened together and all the soldiers the Princess had killed came to life again—but their beards had grown so long that they almost swept the floor!

So, when the King came to the church, it was all full of soldiers, and at the door he met Frederick and the Princess. She was so beautiful that he could not believe she was his daughter; and, when she told him that Frederick had set her free, he gave her to him in marriage.

The very same day the King had a great feast prepared at which all the soldiers got plenty to eat, for they were very hungry.

And Frederick himself became King when the old King died.

ST. PETER'S MOTHER

WHEN St. Peter got to Heaven he saw that his mother was still in Purgatory. He felt very sad and pleaded, 'Dear Lord, let me free my mother from Purgatory.' And his request was granted.

Now, when St. Peter rose with her from Purgatory to journey up to Heaven, many poor souls clung to her skirt, hoping to rise with her. But she was grudging, and shook them off. So they all dropped back. When St. Peter saw this he knew his mother's heart to be wicked, and let go of her again. Then back she fell to Purgatory, where she may be still if her heart hasn't softened since.

BLUEBEARD

THERE was once a man with three sons and a beautiful
daughter, and they lived in a wood. One day a golden
carriage arrived, drawn by six horses and with many footmen
and pages, and down stepped a King, who asked the man for
his daughter's hand. Pleased at his child's good fortune, the man
readily gave his consent. Indeed the suitor had but one fault—
his beard was all blue, and people quaked at the sight of him.

The girl was at first afraid and held back from marrying the
King, but her father pleaded with her till at last she agreed to
the match. All the same she felt strangely uneasy, and took
secret counsel with her three brothers. 'My dear brothers,' she
said, 'if ever you hear me call for help, I beg of you, no matter
where you may be, to leave all and come to my aid.' This her
brothers promised, saying, as they kissed her, 'Good bye, dear
sister, and rest assured, if ever we hear your voice, we'll jump on
our horses and be with you soon.'

The girl then got into the carriage, took her seat beside Blue
beard, and drove off with him. Arriving at the castle she found
everything wonderful; indeed, whatever the new Queen asked
for was at once done. Altogether the royal couple would have
been perfectly happy—if she could only have got used to his
blue beard; but every time her eyes fell upon it she shuddered.

This was how things were for some time; then one day the
King said to her, 'I must go a long journey. Here are the keys of
the whole castle, and you may open all the doors and look at
anything you like—except for the small room opened with this
little gold key. That room is forbidden, and if you unlock the
door it will cost you your life.'

The girl took the keys and promised to obey.

Now as soon as the King was gone she unlocked one door
after another, to find so many rich and splendid things that they
seemed to have come from every corner of the world. At last

nothing was left but the forbidden room; and, since its key was of gold, she fancied that perhaps the greatest treasure of all might be stored there. More and more curious, she would have given all she had seen so far just for one peep into that room.

For a while she resisted temptation, but so strong did it grow in the end that she took the key and hurried to the forbidden door. 'Anyway, who will know that I have opened it?' she said to herself; 'I'll only peep inside.' Then she put the key into the lock. As the door opened, a stream of blood rushed towards her, and she saw hanging round the walls the dead bodies of women —of some only the skeletons were left. Such a fright this gave her that she at once let the door close to again—but the key dropped and fell into the blood. Hastily she picked it up, and tried to wipe the blood off, but it was no use, as, the moment she cleaned it off one side, it appeared again on the other; and, though she sat there the whole day rubbing and doing everything she could think of to remove it, all was in vain, the blood-stains would not go. At last, as evening fell, she hid the key in the hay, hoping that this might dry the blood over-night.

Next day Bluebeard returned, and the first thing he did was to ask for the keys. With her heart beating fast she fetched the bunch, hoping he wouldn't notice that the gold one was missing. But he counted them all and when he was finished asked, 'Where's the one for the secret room?' He was staring her straight in the face, and she blushed crimson as she answered, 'Oh, that one! it's upstairs—I mislaid it—I'll look for it in the morning.' But the King said, 'You'd better look now, dear wife, as I'll need it today.' 'Then I may as well admit it, I've lost it in the hay and will have to look for it first.'

'You have not lost it,' stormed Bluebeard; 'you've stuffed it in there to dry off the blood, for you haven't obeyed my order but gone into the room. Well, now you shall go into it whether you like to or not!'

So she had to go and fetch the key, still covered with blood, while Bluebeard roared, 'Make ready to die, for die you shall this very day.' And taking out his great knife he dragged her along the hall.

'Oh, please let me say a prayer before I die,' she pleaded.

'All right,' he answered; 'but be quick about it—I won't wait long.'

At that she raced up the stairway and cried out of the window at the top of her voice, 'My brothers, dear brothers, come, help me!'

Just then her brothers were sitting in the wood, drinking some cool wine. All of a sudden the youngest cried, 'I think I hear our sister's voice. Come, we must hurry to her aid.' So they leapt on their horses and rode off like the wind.

Their sister, meanwhile, was down on her knees, in terror. Then Bluebeard yelled up from below, 'Aren't you ready yet?' And she could hear him sharpening his knife on the bottom step. She looked out but saw nothing except a cloud of dust in the distance as of a flock driven along. So again she cried, 'My brothers, dear brothers, come, help me!'

Then Bluebeard roared, 'If you don't come down this instant, I'll drag you! I've got the knife sharp now!'

Again she scanned the distance, and this time she caught sight of her three brothers galloping across the fields, cleaving the air like birds; and in desperation she cried for the third time as loudly as she could, 'My brothers, dear brothers, come, help me!' So near was the youngest by this, that she could hear him calling, 'Take heart, dear sister, another moment and we'll be with you!'

Then Bluebeard roared again, 'Enough of your prayers! I'll not wait any longer—if you don't come now, I'll fetch you!' She answered, 'Oh, just let me pray for my three brothers!' but not heeding her he rushed up the stairs, and dragged her down. He had just seized her by the hair, and was on the point of stabbing her to the heart, when the three brothers beat down the

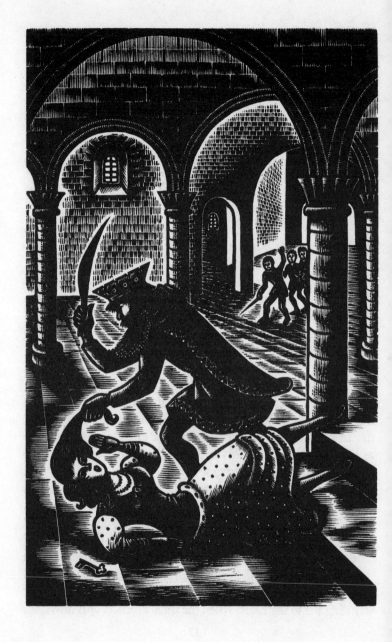

door, burst in and snatched her from his grasp. Then they drew their swords and struck him down.

The brothers hung his body up in the blood-chamber, alongside the remains of the women he had slain. Then they took their dearest sister home; and all Bluebeard's riches became hers.

WHY DOGS DISLIKE CATS AND CATS DISLIKE MICE

A DOG had served a lion faithfully for many years, and so the King of the Animals wished to honour his devoted servant. One day he said to the dog, 'Hearken to me: from this day onwards you shall be one of my nobles!' And he gave him a patent of nobility, drawn up on parchment in handsome lettering all decorated with gold.

The faithful dog was delighted, went off to the cat, his great friend, and said, 'Good cousin, the King has conferred a high honour on me. To this end he has given me a parchment in handsome lettering all decorated with gold. Will you be good enough to store this parchment for me, and keep a sharp eye on it to see it doesn't get damaged or stolen, till the day I come back and fetch it.'

The cat, promising to do so, hid the parchment down a hole in a great oak-tree, where it seemed quite safe. To satisfy the dog, the cat at first kept regular watch over it, to make sure it did not get damaged by rain; but in time she forgot all about it, and just left it alone.

Meanwhile a hungry little mouse, happening to come across the parchment, nibbled at it every day till at length it was all tattered and torn.

At last the dog came to the cat and asked for his parchment, as he had to take it with him to a tournament at the Royal Court.

So the cat discovered the ruin wrought in the hollow tree by the mouse.

Furious at what had happened, the cat swore everlasting war on the mouse, and the dog likewise on the cat. And from that time on they have never been able to bear each other.

WHY DOGS SNIFF ONE ANOTHER

DURING a feast given by the lion, to which most of the animals had been invited, it was found that the pepper was missing. The lion at once called a dog who was sitting with them at the high table, and asked him to run quickly to the next town and fetch some pepper.

The dog growled with vexation at leaving behind so many delicious morsels; all the same he went off, as otherwise he would have got a beating. But, instead of fetching the pepper, he played a trick—and ran away with it.

So they waited for an hour, and another hour, but no dog turned up! This made the lion angry, and he sent the other dogs out to search for the one with the pepper. Wherever they found him they were to tear him in pieces; and so long as they didn't find the dog with the pepper and pay him out for it they would only get bones—and not meat—at the royal table.

From that very day dogs sniff one another to find the dog with the pepper. But they haven't found him yet.

THE FAITHFUL LITTLE DOVE

ONCE upon a time there was a man who had a wife and a daughter. He had sent them to live in houses far apart so that they couldn't see each other. He treated them harshly; for he had no love for them.

Now the mother had a friend who kept a little dove, which he often took with him when visiting the daughter; so it learnt to know the way. One day the little dove came flying all alone to the daughter, who thought it must have escaped. Its wings were drooping, and, when the daughter looked closely, she found a tiny letter tied to one of them; it was from her mother. She was very pleased, and in return hung a few lines to her mother on the little dove's wing before letting the bird fly away.

This happened again and again, and one day the little dove came with a note saying the mother was very ill and wished to see her daughter, who should just follow the dove. So that very night she set out and followed the little dove. But the father got to know, sent after her and had her brought back and locked up again.

Then one day the little dove came back carrying in its beak a green twig from the mother's grave. The daughter grieved so much over this that she, too, died.

When she was buried, the little dove fetched another twig from the mother's grave, put it on the daughter's, then lay down beside it and died also.

THE MOON AND HER MOTHER

ONE fine day the Moon asked her Mother for a warm frock; the nights were cold, she said. The Mother took her measurements, and the girl ran off.

In a short while the Moon came back but, as she had grown so big that the little frock no longer fitted her, her Mother began undoing the seams and letting them out. The girl grew impatient and again ran off, but her Mother got busy sewing, sitting up many nights in the light of the stars.

At length the Moon came back again, but, having run a

lot, she had lost weight and was pale and thin; so the frock was far too big now, and the sleeves came down to her knees.

By this time the Mother had had enough of it, and very angry with these tricks she cried, 'You needn't come back to me for a frock—ever!'

So, up to this very day, the bad little girl is forced to run about without a stitch on, until some kind person comes along and buys a frock for her.

THE HAND WITH THE KNIFE

THERE was once a little girl who had three brothers, and they meant everything to her mother, while she herself always came last. She was spoken to harshly, and had to get out early, morning after morning, to dig peat from the dry soil of the heath—they needed it for the fires and for cooking. Yet all they gave her to do this hard work with was an old blunt shovel.

Now the little girl had a lover, a fairy who lived in a hill close to her mother's house. Each time she passed the hill, the fairy stretched his hand from the rock and held out a very sharp knife. It had special powers and would cut through anything. With it she quickly dug the peat, and returned home with her bundle happily. As she passed the rock she knocked twice, then out came the hand and took back the knife.

But when the mother saw how she brought the peat home quickly and without trouble, she told the brothers, saying that surely somebody must be helping the girl or she couldn't do it. Then the brothers stole after her and saw how she got the magic knife. They caught up with her and forced it out of her grasp. Then they went back and knocked on the rock as she was wont to do. But when the good fairy stretched out his hand, they struck it off with his own knife.

The bleeding arm passed from sight; and as the fairy thought it was the girl herself who had betrayed him, he never showed himself again.

THE PINK

THERE was once a King whose mind was made up never to marry. Then one day he happened to stand at a window watching the people go to church, and among them was a girl of such beauty that, in a single moment, his mind was changed, and he called the girl in and asked her to become his wife.

When a year had passed, the Queen gave birth to a Prince. The King could not think whom to invite as godfather, till at last he decided: 'The first person I meet, whoever it may be, I'll ask to be the godfather.' So he went out; the first person he met was a poor old man, and he invited him. The poor man consented, but begged to be allowed to carry the baby into the church alone: the doors must be locked, and nobody permitted to watch. His request was granted.

Now the King had a wicked prying gardener, and when the old man carried the child into the church, this fellow stole in after him and hid behind the pews. He saw the old man bear the child before the altar. There he blessed it, and, as if possessing magic power, he promised that all the child ever wished for should come true. Upon this the wicked gardener thought how greatly it would profit him to get hold of the child.

Now one day when the Queen was walking in the garden carrying the baby in her arms, the gardener snatched him from her. He smeared the Queen's mouth with the blood of a chicken, then swore before the King that he had seen her slay her own child in the garden and eat him. The King had her thrown into prison, while the gardener sent the child far away to a forester in the woods, who was to bring him up.

There the Prince learnt to hunt. The forester had a beautiful daughter called Lisa, and the two children loved each other. Lisa told the boy one day he was a Prince, and all he wished for would come true. Soon after, the gardener came to see the forester, and when the Prince caught sight of him he wished him turned into a poodle; but his dear Lisa he changed into a flower—a pink—which he put into his buttonhole. The poodle had to trot along beside him.

Then the Prince made his way to his father's Court and took service as one of the royal huntsmen. Soon the King liked him better than any of the others, for he was such a good marksman that he could hit any deer—he had only to wish and it would come bounding right in front of him. The only reward he asked for his services was a room to himself. He always kept it locked, and made his own meals.

His comrades thought it odd that he served without pay, and so one of them stole after him and peeped through the keyhole. He saw the new huntsman sitting before a table laden with the finest food, and beside him a beautiful girl; and they seemed greatly to enjoy each other's company. Of course, the meal had been simply wished on to the table by the Prince, and the girl was his dear Lisa changed back to her proper shape. He liked to have her with him the moment he was alone, but when he was out she once more became a pink, standing in a glass of water. However, the huntsmen thought he must be rich, and they broke into the room when he was away hunting; but all they found was the pink standing on the window-sill. Yet the flower looked so lovely that they took it to show the King, who was charmed with it and asked his huntsman to give it to him. But he would not part with it for all the gold in the world—wasn't the flower his dearest Lisa?

At length, when the King would brook no denial, the Prince confessed the whole story, revealing that he was his son. On hearing this the King was filled with joy, he freed the Queen from prison, and faithful Lisa became the Prince's wife. As punishment the wicked gardener remained a poodle for life, and the servants always drove him under the table.

A TALL STORY

THERE was once a King who made it known that the man who could tell the tallest story should marry his daughter. All the gentlemen of the Court tried one after another, but their stories were too tame—not one could tell a thumping good lie.

Then a poor country lad came before the King and said, 'Your Majesty, in our garden we once had a cabbage. It grew bigger and bigger, till in the end its leaves reached up to the very sky. So I climbed it to get a peep into Heaven. The gates happened to be open, and I beheld such brightness and glory that there and then I wanted to jump inside; but the gates were shut in my face, and there was I left, hanging in the clouds. However, I began to let myself down on a rope—till, when I was halfway to safety, the rope snapped and I hurtled sheer down and landed right on a pebble! In the twinkling of an eye I had thought out a plan, and ran home, fetched an axe, and with one blow freed myself.'

'Now that's a thumping big lie,' cried the King; 'it's the biggest lie I've heard in my life!'

'All the better,' put in the yokel, 'for now your daughter is mine!'

At these words the King shook in his shoes; and, to get rid of the boy, he gave him a good pile of money.

Now that just suited the lad, for he had seen the Princess: she had bleary eyes and was dreadfully ugly.

THE OLD WITCH

THERE was once a King who loved horses above all things. In his stables the horses fed from marble mangers and were watered out of silver buckets. All the King's courtiers wore riding-boots and spurs, and under their arms they carried whips. At the Court balls the favourite dances were gallops; and all the King would say was, 'Gee up!' or 'Wo! stand still, old man!'

Now the King had two fair daughters, Mene and Bene: the elder was wicked, but the young one was good. One day Mene was walking in the wood and, as she sat down under a tree to rest, a golden key suddenly shot up out of the ground and began dancing round her, first in big and then in smaller and smaller circles. In the end it sprang into her hand and pulled the Princess off her seat; and, as her hand was somehow fixed to the key, try as she might she could not tear herself away, but was dragged across the wood to a rock. There the key jumped out of the girl's hand into a keyhole, and lo and behold! the rock opened into a large and splendid room, where behind a web of gold lay a sleeping Prince. Written up on a board beside him were the words: 'Who wants to win him must first love an ugly monster.' Mene tried with all her might to tear down the golden web, but in an instant all the splendour vanished and a howling gale drove her out of the rock.

On her way home she met her sister, whom she hated. She noticed how a little, many-coloured bird circled round her sister and dropped a jewel from its beak, but she could not catch the words the bird was singing:

'Keep this little gem, and guard it well:
Some day, in your need, hope it will spell!'

Mene hurried greedily forward crying, 'What have you got there? Give it to me.' Bene showed her the jewel, but, as she would not give it up, Mene began quarrelling. 'Be quiet! It belongs to Bene,' a voice behind them broke in; and, on turning round, they saw a hunchbacked dwarf and were afraid. For her own ends Mene put on a friendly face, thinking that the dwarf might help her win the handsome sleeping Prince. But the dwarf ran back to the wood.

Then Bene, sorry to see her wicked sister mocking the dwarf behind his back, decided to look for him and tell him. She found him and warned him. The dwarf, hopping after her on one leg, could not catch up with Bene again; and as she ran, she let her precious jewel fall.

Now, walking through a narrow cutting she came across an old witch, who cried, 'Don't knock into me, my beautiful child!' Bene tried her hardest to get past without touching her, but the old woman kept swaying from side to side till the Princess felt quite dizzy and in the end they crashed into each other. 'I wish the earth would swallow you up, you wicked thing!' shrieked the witch, then burst into pieces like a broken pot, right at Bene's feet—an arm here, a leg there, nothing left joined, and all the bits mixed up. In the midst lay the witch's head, which began to speak, saying, 'You wicked child, put me together again at once—take my right leg and lean it carefully against a stone, then take the left one and do the same. But be careful they don't run away. Be sharp about it, put everything together properly and don't forget one single piece.'

At this Bene was terrified and wanted to run away, but the head stood itself in front of her. So the Princess began putting the old witch together; and all the bits fitted quite easily. When at last she had stuck the arms on to the trunk, the head jumped into place of itself, and there stood the broken old witch, whole once more. She picked up her stick, and shook hands with the Princess, saying, 'Goodbye, my little daughter, I forgive you because you've put me together again so nicely; and I'll make you some return, too: you shall have a handsome husband.'

Bene now went away to search for her lost jewel, but the little bird brought it back to her, singing the while:

'Pray keep it safe, the precious little stone,
When I fly away you must guard it alone.
Had you not lost it you well might have laughed
At the old woman's tricks and her evil craft!'

Now the old Queen, at Mene's request, had the ugly dwarf invited to the Court; but the King scorned him as a son-in-law, and even the Queen and Mene mocked him behind his back. Then Bene went out into the wood and wept, and again she met the old witch, who told her her bridegroom had arrived. But it was a silly fop of a Prince who came striding up, and, as she could not bear him, she went sadly back to the garden. Here she found the ugly but wise old dwarf, and poured her heart out to him. They talked and talked, till at last he asked her if she despised him as all the rest did. 'No, no,' said Bene, 'for I love you.' At that the magic spell was broken, and the dwarf turned into a fine young man. Then he told his story—how once, in the woods, because he had knocked against the witch and laughed at her strange capers, she had cast a spell upon him. This could only be broken if a beautiful girl, of her own free will, loved him in his ugly guise. For some of the time he had had to sleep in the rock in his old shape.

As he was speaking, the witch came from the castle into the garden, and with her was her silly fop of a son and the rest of the party. She thrust her bony hand into the girl's golden hair and carried her off like a feather through the air, over hills and valleys, for over a hundred miles, till they came to a round tower of iron. In the tower was nothing to be seen but snails, creeping up and down the walls. 'Here you shall stay; and if within a week you haven't taught these snails to dance, you shall be turned into one yourself!'

When the witch was gone, locking the door behind her, the

snails were afraid of the Princess and drew back into their little houses. By and by, however, they came out again, and made friends with her. An unseen hand brought food for her and green grass for the snails, and they whiled away the hours; but time passed dreadfully slowly in the tower.

Six days went by and still Bene had no idea how to teach the snails to dance, but on the morning of the seventh the little bird came to the window and sang:

> 'For the last time bear I the precious stone:
> Be mindful you're its guardian alone!'

Now that she had got the lost gem back, she noticed a narrow slit in it, and out of this jumped twelve tiny dancing-masters, each as long as a finger, carrying tiny fiddles. The instant they started tuning up, the snails crept out of their houses and began waltzing in couples. In the end the little dancing-masters leapt back into the jewel; but one left his fiddle behind, and the Princess picked it up. The moment she began playing the snails began to dance.

The Prince, meanwhile, had wandered far and wide in search of his loved one without finding her. On the morning of the eighth day he was still a hundred miles from the iron tower, when suddenly he saw a brand-new pair of boots standing in the grass by the wayside. His own being badly worn he put on the new boots, then he had hardly taken a step before he found himself in strange country, his second step covered a wide valley and a broad stream, and the third a whole city with tall towers: in short, with every step he covered a mile. On he went, and in a hundred steps he stood before the iron tower.

Just then the old witch was watching the snails dance. She was furious to see they were doing so well, and made lots of excuses still not to set the Princess free. Sadly, Bene went to the window, but she was overjoyed when she saw her lover below. She threw him down the gem, which, the moment he picked it up, changed into a shining sword. With it he touched the gate, which sprang wide open. When the Prince entered, the witch fled to the corner where the snails were. When he touched them with the sword they changed into fair maidens. Then he slew the witch.

The old King took to his son-in-law, with his fine seven-league boots, for he could ride the wildest of the royal horses.

NOTES

PEOPLE mentioned in the Notes:

BRENTANO, Clemens (1778-1842): German Romantic poet, brother of Bettina (1785-1859), who became the wife of Achim von Arnim (1781-1831), another Romantic poet, who encouraged the Grimms to publish their fairy-tale collection.

THE HASSENPFLUGS: a family in the Cassel circle; they were keen collaborators with the Grimms. A son, Ludwig, later married the Grimms' sister Lotte. Madame Hassenpflug was of French descent.

THE VON HAXTHAUSENS and the VON DROSTE-HÜLSHOFFS: families of the Westphalian aristocracy and contributors to the tale-collecting. Annette von Droste-Hülshoff (1797-1848) ranks as the best German poetess of the nineteenth century.

THE WILDS: a Swiss family settled in Cassel, and neighbours of the Grimms. They contributed many stories to the Grimm collection. Particularly helpful were Gretchen, Lisette and Dortchen, who became the wife of Wilhelm Grimm. The Wilds' maid—'die alte Marie'—was an outstanding teller of folk tales.

ABBREVIATIONS used in the Notes:

AKH: *Anmerkungen zu den Kinder- und Hausmärchen der Brüder Grimm.* The edition date is specified in each instance.

DE: Definitive Edition of the Tales, viz. the seventh, 1857.

KH: *Kinder- und Hausmärchen der Brüder Grimm.* Date specified.

KHi: as above, first edition, volume i, 1812.

KHii: „ , first edition, volume ii, 1815.

NOTES ON THE TALES:

MAKE-ME-SHUDDER: *Der Fürchtemich.* Source: AKH, 1856. Told, between 1812 and 1815, by the Fairy Tale Wife, Katherina Viehmann, of Niederzwehren near Cassel. Cf. 'The Story of the Youth Who Went Forth to Learn What Fear Is,' DE no. 4.

THE FROG PRINCE: *Der Froschprinz.* Source: KHii no. 13. Told by Old Marie in the Wilds' house in Cassel, 1813. Omitted in subsequent editions, though a typical example of the three-times motive. Cf. 'The Frog King,' DE no. 1, taken down in 1810 in Hesse.

THE NIGHTINGALE AND THE SLOW-WORM: *Von der Nachtigall und der Blindschleiche.* Source: KHi no. 6. Taken from *Les Mémoires de l'académie celtique,* 1808; described as being told in the Sologne district of the Upper Loire. Omitted in subsequent editions. The belief that birds and other animals could change eyes is referred to in 'Romeo and Juliet,' III. v. 31.

BEAUTIFUL CATHARINELLA: *Die Schöne Katharinella.* Source: Grimm MSS. Written down by Lulu Jordis, sister of Clemens Brentano, in 1814, as remembered from her childhood. Jacob Grimm, writing to Wilhelm from Paris, 1 June 1814, announced its dispatch: 'From Madame Jordis you will receive within a day or two a letter with two fairy tales (slightly polished, I believe).' Most likely from Italian tradition, current with the Brentano family, originally from Tremezzo. Cf. 'Rapunzel,' DE no. 12, from Hesse.

HANS FRANK: *Hans Franke.* Source: Grimm MSS. Related, about 1843, to Wilhelm Grimm by Ludwig Konrad Bethmann, a Wolfenbüttel librarian. The motive of the good and the bad sisters occurs also in 'Mother Holle,' DE no. 24.

THE PRINCESS ON THE GLASS MOUNTAIN: *Die Prinzessin auf dem Glasberg.* Source: Grimm MSS. Obtained by Jacob Grimm, before October 1810, from the Hanau district. The glass-mountain motive frequently recurs, cf. DE nos. 25, 93, 127, 193, 196, viz. 'The Seven Ravens,' 'The Raven,' 'The Iron Stove,' 'The Drummer,' 'Rinkrank'.

DEATH AND THE GOOSEHERD: *Der Tod und der Gänsehirt.* Source: KHi no. 27. Taken from Harsdörfer, *Der grosse Schauplatz jämmerlicher Mordgeschichten,* 1663. Omitted in subsequent editions.

THE PHOENIX: *Vogel Phönix.* Source: KHi no. 75. Told in 1812, from tradition in the Main region, by Old Marie in the Wilds' house in Cassel. Replaced in the second edition by a Fairy Tale Wife story: 'The Devil with the Three Golden Hairs,' no. 29.

PUSS-IN-BOOTS: *Der gestiefelte Kater.* Source: KHi no. 33. Told in 1812 by Jeanette Hassenpflug in Cassel. Omitted in subsequent editions because of resemblance to Perrault's *Le Maître Chat ou le Chat Botté,* of which German translations abounded. The motive occurs in older Italian collections also.

SIMPLE HANS: *Hans Dumm.* Source: KHi no. 54. Told in 1812 in the Hassenpflugs' house in Cassel. Omitted in subsequent editions. The motive goes back to stories in Basile's *Pentamerone,* 1634-6, and further back still to Straparola's collection, 1550.

THE LOVELY FLORANDINE: *Die allerschönste Florandine.* Source: Grimm MSS. Told by Martchen Luckhard, daughter of a Cassel bookseller, to Amalie Hassenpflug, who sent it to the Grimms in 1836. The forbidden door motive occurs widely; cf. 'The Two Brothers,' 'Our Lady's Child' and 'Fitcher's Bird,' DE nos. 60, 3, 46.

MASTER EVER READY: *Herr Fix und Fertig.* Source: KHi no. 16. Told by Friedrich Krause, the sergeant of dragoons, in 1811, as a spinning-room tale and taken down in Hoof in the Habichtswald. Omitted in subsequent editions; cf. the Hessian tale, 'The Queen Bee,' DE no. 62.

PRINCESS MOUSE-SKIN: *Prinzessin Mäusehaut.* Source: KHi no. 71. Taken down by Wilhelm Grimm about 1810 from tales told by Jeanette Hassenpflug in Cassel. Omitted in subsequent editions because of affinity with Charles Perrault's *Peau d'Ane.* Cf. 'Allerleirauh,' DE no. 65.

THE OGRE: *Der Okerlo.* Source: KHi no. 70. Told in Cassel, between 1810 and 1812, by Jeanette Hassenpflug. Omitted in subsequent editions for its affinity with *Der Riesen-wald,* in *Feenmärchen,* Braunschweig, 1801.

THE CRAFTY WOLF: *Der listige Wolf.* Source: Grimm MSS. Received from Bavaria before 1822. Cf. DE no. 73, in which the animals have interchanged roles.

THE WOODEN HORSE: *Das Hölzerne Pferd.* Source: Grimm MSS. Taken down by the philologist Franz Joseph Mone, about 1820, probably in the Baden district. Has oriental affinities.

THE THREE SISTERS: *Die Drei Schwestern.* Source: KHi no. 82. Adapted, with touches from oral tradition, from a tale in Musäeus's *Volksmärchen.* Omitted from subsequent editions. The animal brothers-in-law motive occurs in 'The Crystal Ball,' DE no. 197.

THE SHOEMAKER AND THE TAILOR: *Vun den Schoster un den Snider.* Source: Grimm MSS. Brought in 1842 from Holstein by Main, a Kiel student. Translated by Wilhelm Grimm out of the Low German, with inevitable shifts of expression, and printed in the fifth edition as 'The Two Travel-lers,' DE no. 107. The translation in the present volume has been made from the original Low German text.

THE RING AND THE LAMP: *Die Lampe und der Ring.* Source: Grimm MSS. Taken down by the Grimms' friend

Paul Wigand, in 1813, in the Weser district. Rejected for resemblance to the Aladdin story. Cf. 'The Blue Light,' DE no. 116.

THE WORKER AND THE DRONE: *Der Faule und der Fleissige*. Source: KHii no. 33. Taken down between 1812 and 1815 in Hesse, probably by Ferdinand Siebert at Treysa. Omitted in subsequent editions.

TWO BROTHERS IN FORTUNE: *Die beiden Glücks-brüder*. Source: Grimm MSS. Taken down from Marie von Dalwigk, in 1828, in Cassel. Cf. 'Donkey Cabbages,' DE no. 122.

PRINCE SWAN: *Prinz Schwan*. Source: KHi no. 59. Taken down by Wilhelm Grimm from Gretchen Wild, 1807, in Cassel. Omitted in subsequent editions. The animal bride-groom motive occurs frequently. Cf. 'The Iron Stove,' DE no. 127.

THE DEVIL AND THE THREE SOLDIERS: *Der Teufel und die drei Soldaten*. Source: AKH, 1822. Probably taken down by Jacob Grimm during his stay in Vienna, 1814/15, from tradition in German Bohemia. Cf. 'The Devil and His Grandmother,' DE no. 125.

THE MUSICIANS ON THE GALLOWS: *De Muse-kanten up de Galge*. Source: Grimm MSS. Taken down before 1816 in the Münster district by the von Droste-Hülshoffs, and sent to the Grimms by the von Haxthausens. Cf. 'The Devil and His Grandmother,' DE no. 125, and 'The Devil and the Three Soldiers' in the present collection.

HURLEBURLEBUTZ: *Hurleburlebutz*. Source: KHi no. 66. Taken down in 1812 by Jeanette Hassenpflug in the Main district. Omitted in subsequent editions. Cf. 'The Iron Stove,' DE no. 127.

THE LION AND THE FROG: *Der Löwe und der Frosch.*
Source: Grimm MSS. Sent to Wilhelm Grimm in 1814 by
Lulu Jordis, Brentano's sister, who had heard her mother tell
it; from the Main. Written up by Wilhelm, it appeared in
KHii as no. 43. Omitted in subsequent editions because of
Jacob's stricture—'etwas interpoliert'.

THE SIMPLETON: *Der einfältige Junge.* Source: AKH,
1822. Taken down, before 1822, in the Paderborn district by
the von Haxthausen family. Cf. 'Going a Travelling,' DE
no. 143.

TWO CHILDREN IN A FAMINE: *Die Kinder in
Hungersnot.* Source: KHii no. 57. Taken, with slight adjust-
ments, from Prätorius, *Abenteurlicher Glückstopf,* 1669. Subsequently omitted.

OUR LADY OF SORROWS: *Die heilige Frau Kummernis.*
Source: KHii no. 66. Taken almost word for word from
Andreas Strobl, *Ovum Paschale,* 1700. Subsequently omitted.
The legend originated in the fifteenth century from a mis-
conception: the Romanesque long-robed figure of Christ was
taken to be a bearded woman.

THE MANIKIN: *Dat klein Männeken.* Source: AKH, 1822.
Taken down in the Paderborn district by the von Haxthausens.

THE PRINCE WHO WAS BEWITCHED: *Der verzau-
berte Königssohn.* Source: Grimm MSS. Transcribed by Jacob
Grimm, in typical folk-tale manner, from Basile's *Pentamerone,*
1634-6.

THE WILLOW WREN: *Der Zaunkönig.* Source: Grimm
MSS. Taken down in the Celle district and sent to the Grimms
in 1838 by the philologist Karl Goedeke. Features appear in
'The Willow Wren,' DE no. 171, from Mecklenburg.

THE ROBBER AND HIS SONS: *Der Räuber und seine
Söhne.* Source: KH, edition 1843, no. 191. Taken from a

German prose tale in a fifteenth century Leipzig MS, as printed by Moritz Haupt in the *Altdeutsche Blätter,* 1836. Omitted in DE. The first tale in the cycle resembles the Ulysses and Polyphemus episode, to which the earliest version (twelfth century) refers.

JOLLY HANS: *Hans Lustig.* Source: AKH, 1822. Received from the Münster district in a transcription sent to the Hassen‑pflugs by the von Droste‑Hülshoffs. Cheating death or the Devil is a very old motive; cf. the variant 'Gambling Hansel,' DE no. 82; and 'Brother Lustig,' DE no. 81.

THE SHROUD: *Das Totenhemd.* Source: Grimm MSS. Taken down in the Paderborn district by the von Haxthausens. Has affinities with the ballad, 'The Unquiet Grave.'

ILL LUCK: *Das Unglück.* Source: KH, edition 1840, no. 175. Taken from Kirchhof's *Wendunmut,* 1563, without the moralising element. Omitted in DE.

THE DEAD MAN AND THE PRINCESS FREED FROM SLAVERY: *Der dankbare Tote und die aus der Sklaverei erlöste Königstochter.* Source: Grimm MSS. Taken down in the Münster district by the von Droste‑Hülshoffs; sent by the von Haxthausens, between 1812 and 1814, to Wilhelm Grimm, who rejected it as 'a story from a book'. Has affinities with 'Dead Man's Thanks' in the present collection.

DEAD MAN'S THANKS: *Des Toten Dank.* Source: Grimm MSS. Taken down in the Münster district by the von Droste‑Hülshoffs and sent by the von Haxthausens between 1812 and 1814.

THE FAITHFUL WIFE: *Die getreue Frau.* Source: Grimm MSS. Taken down in the Münster district by the von Droste‑Hülshoffs and sent by the von Haxthausens between 1812 and 1814. Wilhelm's comment on the MS, viz. 'modern or from printed books' differs from Jacob's, viz. 'comes from the *Gesta Romanorum.*

THE SENTRY AND THE PRINCESS IN THE COFFIN: *Die Prinzessin im Sarge und die Schildwache.* Source: Grimm MSS. Taken down by the von Haxthausens in Westphalia, about 1818. Has affinities with the folk-tale cycle of the wizard's bride; cf. Andersen's 'The Travelling Companion'.

ST. PETER'S MOTHER: *Sankt Peters Mutter.* Source: Grimm MSS. Taken down in the Münster district by the von Droste-Hülshoffs and sent before 1816 by the von Haxthausens.

BLUEBEARD: *Blaubart.* Source: KHi no. 62. Received in autumn 1812 from the Hassenpflug family in Cassel. Omitted in subsequent editions because of resemblance to Perrault's *La Barbe Bleue.* Cf. 'Fitcher's Bird,' DE no. 46.

WHY DOGS DISLIKE CATS AND CATS DISLIKE MICE: *Warum die Hunde den Katzen und die Katzen den Mäusen feind sind.* Source: Grimm MSS. Taken down before 1819 in Bavaria, probably by Ludwig Aurbacher.

WHY DOGS SNIFF ONE ANOTHER: *Warum die Hunde einander beriechen.* Source: Grimm MSS. Taken down before 1819 in Bavaria, probably by Ludwig Aurbacher.

THE FAITHFUL LITTLE DOVE: *Das treue Täubchen.* Source: Grimm MSS. Taken down by Wilhelm's son Hermann as a boy of thirteen from Martchen Luckhard in Cassel, 1841. Comment at the end: 'Martchen has heard it from old Mrs Theiss in Cassel'.

THE MOON AND HER MOTHER: *Der Mond und seine Mutter.* Source: Grimm MSS. Taken before 1810 by Jacob Grimm from *Grotesken, Satyren und Naivitäten auf das Jahr 1806,* Tübingen, 1806.

THE HAND WITH THE KNIFE: *Die Hand mit dem Messer*. Source: KHi no. 8. Adapted by Jacob Grimm from a Gaelic song given in *Essays on the Superstitions of the Highlands of Scotland*, by Mrs Grant of Laggan, 1811. Omitted in subsequent editions.

THE PINK: *Die Nelke*. Source: KHi no. 76. Told, 1812, in Cassel by the Hassenpflugs. Replaced in the second edition, 1819, by a variant told by the Fairy Tale Wife between 1812 and 1815, 'The Pink,' DE no. 76.

A TALL STORY: *Lügenmärchen*. Source: AKH, 1822. Taken down before that date by the von DrosteHülshoffs in the Münster district. The incredible tale motive, exemplified in 'Jack and the Beanstalk,' goes back to ancient times. It appears in 'The Flail from Heaven,' DE no. 112.

THE OLD WITCH: *Die alte Hexe*. Source: Grimm MSS. Taken, before October 1810, by Jacob Grimm from a 'modern and badly told story,' *Der schöne Schläfer*, in Langbein's *Feierabende*, 1794. Wilhelm regarded *König Einbein*, a variant noted in 1813 by Annette von DrosteHülshoff, as 'made up'. The dancing snails motive occurs also in a story in Madame d'Aulnoy's collection.